AUTOMOBILES AND MOTORCYCLES

THE SMITHSONIAN COLLECTION OF AUTOMOBILES AND MOTORCYCLES

SMITH HEMPSTONE OLIVER
and
DONALD H. BERKEBILE

SMITHSONIAN INSTITUTION PRESS

CITY OF WASHINGTON 1968

Smithsonian Publication 4719
(A revision of United States National Museum Bulletins 198 and 213)

Library of Congress Catalog 68-9579

Distributed by Random House, Inc., in the United States and Canada
Designed by Hubert Leckie / Susan Lehmann
Printed in the United States of America

CONTENTS

ABOUT THE EXHIBIT

IN THE SMITHSONIAN INSTITUTION'S COLLECTION of vehicles are more than 40 automobiles, trucks, and self-powered cycles that date from about 1869 to 1964. Only about half of these are exhibited in the Vehicle Hall of the Museum of History and Technology at any one time, but a rotation program assures that all of them may be viewed by the public over a period of a few years.

On the end sheets is a listing of the automobiles, trucks, and powered cycles in the collection as of March 1967. Included in the list are the Museum's completely detailed scale models of a few other automobiles and trucks of historical significance. All of these, plus some others in private collections or other museums, are described and illustrated in this book, which is a revision and expansion of two earlier works, Bulletin 198 and Bulletin 213 of the United States National Museum. Photographs are from Smithsonian negatives except where indicated otherwise.

The 1893-1894 Duryea and 1913 Ford automobiles presently are displayed in the Museum's exhibition hall titled Growth of the United States. At times, other vehicles might be exhibited in various areas of the Museum.

The Museum of History and Technology is open daily (except Christmas) from 9:00 a.m. to 4:30 p.m., and during the months of April through August it remains open until 9:00 p.m. There is no admission charge.

THE AUTOMOTIVE PIONEERS

WHILE AWARE OF THE IMPORTANCE of the self-powered vehicle in our lives today, many of us do not realize how recent was its invention and how rapid has been its development. The probable reason for this is that most of us have seen, used, and received service from such vehicles all of our lives.

Many impractical vehicles, powered by such means as sails, clockwork, pedals, and treadmills, were conceived—if not actually constructed—in the late 17th century and the early 18th century, and existing drawings tell us of the ingenuity of their designers. The earliest predecessors of the automobile and the motorcycle, however, were steam-propelled road vehicles built between the middle of the 18th century and the late years of the 19th century. The first gasoline-powered vehicle, an experimental model, was not built until the 1860s, and gasoline automobiles were not produced commercially in this country until a few years before the start of the 20th century.

This steam-powered vehicle of 1770—based on a design by Nicolas Cugnot—is preserved in the Conservatoire National des Arts et Métiers, Paris.

NICOLAS JOSEPH CUGNOT

One of the earliest known self-propelled road vehicles was constructed in 1769 by Nicolas Joseph Cugnot, a French military engineer. It could carry four passengers, had a steam supply lasting a little over ten minutes, and could attain a speed of about two miles an hour. Cugnot's vehicle was impractical, but it showed that propulsion by steam was a good idea that should be developed further. In the following year, Cugnot's design was adapted by one Brézin, who constructed a similar vehicle intended for the transportation of artillery. Brézin's machine, carefully preserved in the Conservatoire National des Arts et Métiers, in Paris, is powered by a steam engine having two vertical, single-acting cylinders attached to the single front wheel. The engine and copper boiler turn with the wheel when it is steered.

ENGLISH BUILDERS OF ROAD LOCOMOTIVES

Among the many English designers and builders of early steam-propelled vehicles were William Murdock, Richard Trevithick, Sir Goldsworthy Gurney, Sir Charles Dance, Walter Hancock, William Church, and Squire and Maceroni. Between 1786 and 1838 the work of such inventors resulted in the construction of small operable models and the production of road locomotives that transported passengers and freight. Some of these models and vehicles had three wheels, others had four or six, and some of Gurney's had mechanically operated legs for propulsion and used wheels only for support.

One of Walter Hancock's steam carriages, 1836.

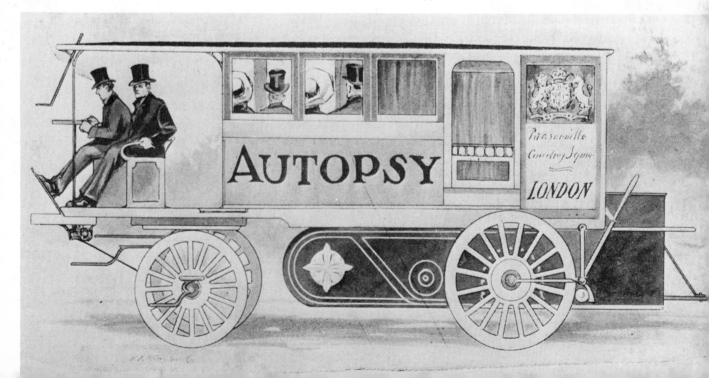

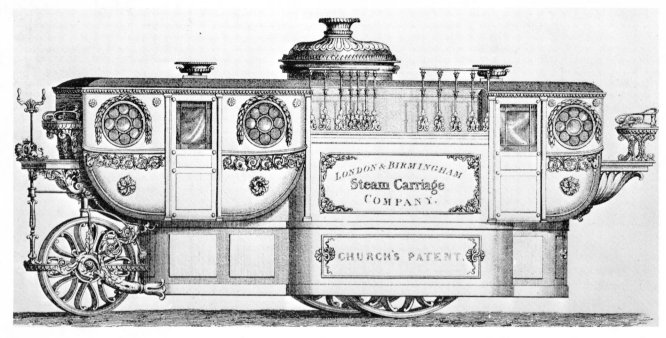

Steam carriage of William Church, 1832.

In the Science Museum at South Kensington is a copy of a small 3-wheel model that William Murdock built prior to 1786. There is evidence that Murdock constructed other models but that he abandoned his experiments because of pressure brought by his employers, Boulton and Watt. Also in the museum at South Kensington is a 3-wheel model that was built about 1797 by Richard Trevithick, whose full-size steamers operated on the roads of Camborne in Cornwall in 1801 and on the streets of London in 1803.

Among several types of steam-powered vehicles constructed by Gurney between 1825 and 1829 were steam-propelled tractors that he used for pulling conventional carriages. These conveyances were taken over and improved upon by Dance, who, from February to June 1831, ran them four times a day in a regular service between Gloucester and Cheltenham, a distance of nine miles that was covered at an average speed of slightly over ten miles an hour, including stops.

Between 1827 and 1838 Walter Hancock built nine steam carriages of various types, all of which were mechanically successful. In 1832 he started a regular steam omnibus service between Paddington and London. One of his better carriages weighed about 7,000 pounds and carried 16 passengers. Two vertical cylinders, nine inches in diameter and with a 12-inch stroke, drove a crankshaft connected by chain to driving wheels 48 inches in diameter. Steam was supplied by a sheet-flue boiler, two feet square and three feet high, that was situated over a grate having a closed ashpit and a fan draft.

Church's steam carriages ran between London and Birmingham in 1832, but competition from a newly opened railroad soon forced discontinuance of the service.

The steam carriages of Squire and Maceroni, built about 1833, had a maximum speed of 20 miles an hour but they regularly ran at an average speed of 14.

By 1836 steam road carriages practically had been abandoned in England because of railroad competition and heavy highway tolls imposed on mechanically propelled vehicles. Their use declined further in 1865 when legislation restricted their speed to four miles an hour in the open country and two miles in the city and required that each vehicle be preceded by a man carrying a red flag. An amendment in 1878 eliminated the flag (but not the man) as a requirement; and in 1896 the popularly called Emancipation Act eliminated the man and raised the speed limit, thus removing major obstacles to the manufacture and use of the automobile in England. By 1903 the speed limit had been raised to 20 miles an hour.

FIRST ATTEMPTS IN AMERICA

Nathan Read, a well-known inventor in Salem, Massachusetts, obtained a patent in 1790 for a 4-wheel vehicle to be powered by a 2-cylinder steam engine. He built a small operable model but progressed no further because there was little public interest in his vehicle.

The earliest known passenger-carrying, self-propelled land vehicle in the United States was produced by Oliver Evans, inventor and engineer. Although Evans had planned a "steam wagon" in 1801, it was not until July 1805 that his "Orukter Amphibolos," or "Amphibious Digger," traveled up Market Street and around the Center Square waterworks in Philadelphia and thus earned the present-day title of "America's first automobile."

The "Orukter Amphibolos," Oliver Evans' steam dredge of 1805, as represented by a model constructed by Greville Bathe.

Built as a steam-operated dredge to be used in the harbor, the 40,000-pound craft was mounted upon axles and wheels, and, propelled by its engine, was steered from its construction site to the water's edge.

It has been stated that the "Johnson brothers," proprietors of an engineering establishment in Philadelphia, built a 4-wheel, 1-cylinder, steam-propelled wagon in 1828. If this could be authenticated, the Johnsons' vehicle would be considered America's first full-sized automobile built specifically to operate on the highway. Also, it has been stated that William James, a stove manufacturer in New York, built in 1830 a 3-wheel steam carriage that was steered by the single front wheel and was powered by a 2-cylinder horizontal engine that drove the rear wheels. No relics of the model built by Read, the steam dredge built by Evans, and the vehicles said to have been built by the Johnsons and by James are known to exist.

Steam-operated tractors that were built in America and abroad in the middle part of the 19th century could be called automobiles in that they moved under their own power, could be steered, and were capable of carrying passengers. Such machines, however, are not properly a part of the history of the automobile because they were designed to perform work in the fields and usually were equipped with broad, cleated wheels, or tracks. Their modern counterparts are diesel-powered tractors.

RICHARD DUDGEON

Probably the oldest surviving self-propelled road conveyance in America is a wooden-wheel, 10-passenger steam carriage built by Richard Dudgeon in New York about 1867. Its two rear wheels are connected to steam cylinders mounted at the front and on each side of a horizontal boiler. Except for having its front axle pivoted for steering and its wheels unflanged, Dudgeon's road locomotive is quite similar to the rail locomotive of its day.

This vehicle, still in operable condition, is in the private collection of George H. Waterman and Kirkland Gibson of East Greenwich, Rhode Island.

An earlier Dudgeon steamer, built about 1853, was destroyed in the fire that consumed New York's Crystal Palace in 1858.

SYLVESTER H. ROPER

In about 1869, Sylvester H. Roper of Roxbury, Massachusetts, built a steam-operated, wooden-wheel velocipede, and later he constructed several steam-propelled wagons.

Roper's 2-wheel velocipede—now in the Museum of History and Technology—was propelled through the rear-wheel axle, which was fitted with cranks connected to two small steam cylinders, one on each side of the rear section of the frame.

Richard Dudgeon's steam vehicle of about 1867 as illustrated in an 1870 catalog of the Dudgeon Company, machinery manufacturer.

THE GREATEST
MECHANICAL
EXHIBITION
IN THE WORLD.

THE
STEAM
BUGGY!

Pronounced by scientific men to be the most wonderful invention of modern times. It can be driven, with two persons in it, 150 miles a day, upon common roads. It is light and strong, and can be managed better than any horse, and can be driven faster than any person dare to ride. Will match it against any trotting horse in the world.

THE ONLY
Steam Velocipede
IN THE WORLD.

Pronounced a perfect triumph in mechanism. It can be driven up any hill, and will out speed any horse in the world.

TO BE SEEN AT
600 BROADWAY.

ADMISSION .... 25 Cents.

An early handbill publicizing Roper steam vehicles.

The Roper steam carriage shown here is in the Henry Ford Museum, Dearborn, Michigan.

One of Roper's steam wagons is now displayed in the Henry Ford Museum at Dearborn, Michigan. This machine, which for several years was exhibited with the Roper velocipede at fairs and circuses in New England, erroneously has been referred to as an Austin steamer because, years ago, it was exhibited for a while by a "Professor" W. W. Austin. Its date of construction is not known.

Roper met his death on June 1, 1896, while operating his newest steam vehicle, another two-wheeler, on the Charles River bicycle track at Cambridge, Massachusetts. That velocipede is now on exhibit at Bellm's Cars of Yesterday, a museum at Sarasota, Florida.

LUCIUS D. COPELAND

In 1883 or 1884 Lucius D. Copeland successfully operated a Star bicycle which he had equipped with a 1-cylinder steam engine and a boiler. Two or three years later, the Northrop Manufacturing Company, of Camden, New Jersey, equipped a tricycle for him in a similar manner. Articles on these machines appeared in many engineering magazines of the time, and Sandford Northrop's associates issued a number of brochures publicizing the formation of their Moto-Cycle Manufacturing Company, a venture which met the fate of other early attempts to produce a commercially successful self-propelled road vehicle in America.

The only known relics of Copeland's machines are the boiler and engine of the Star bicycle, both in the Arizona Museum at Phoenix.

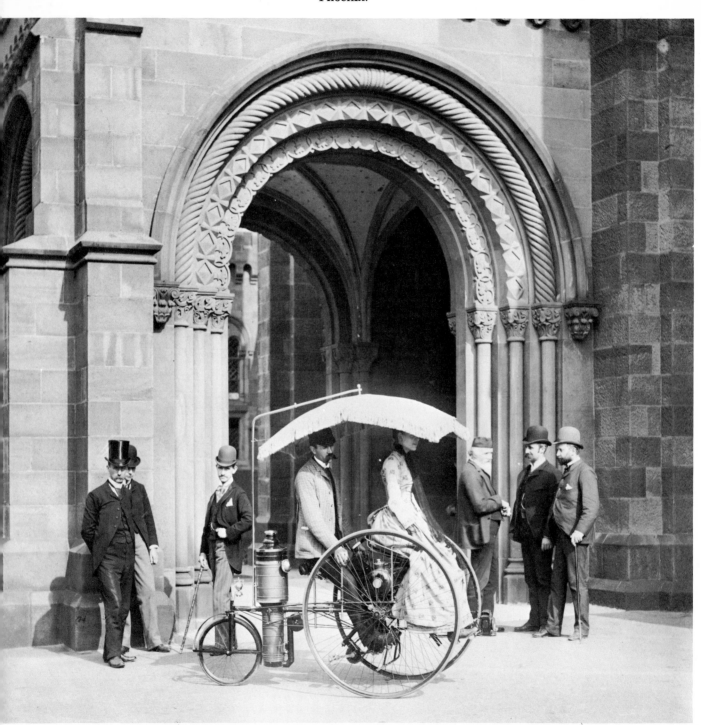

PHAETON MOTO-CYCLE

WEIGHT, 220 POUNDS.
SPEED, 10 MILES PER HOUR.
POWER, 2 HORSE.

MOTO-CYCLE MANUFACTURING COMPANY,

J. E. WATKINS, PRESIDENT,
W. H. TRAVIS, SECRETARY,
E. F. SMITH, TREASURER.

1529 Arch Street, Philadelphia, Pa.

Advertising circular for the Copeland steam tricycle. Note the warning bell at front and rear. Such a bell appears at rear of machine in the preceding illustration.

Lucius D. Copeland and his steam bicycle of the mid-1880s.

Lucius Copeland's steam tricycle at entrance to Smithsonian Building, about 1888. Copeland is at the controls; Sandford Northrop stands behind the small wheel; and at far right is J. Elfreth Watkins, who was curator of transportation and engineering at the Smithsonian at one time.

FROM STEAM TO GASOLINE

Several steam automobiles of fairly advanced design were constructed in France in the latter part of the 19th century. Notable among the inventors of these vehicles were Amédée Bollée, Albert de Dion, and Léon Serpollet. Bollée's first machine, completed in 1873, was followed by improved models of various sizes built by his son as well as himself. All were successful, and some of them attained considerable speed over the roads. Some of the Bollée steamers may be seen today in the Conservatoire at Paris and in the Musée de la Voiture at Compiègne.

The first automobile to be powered by an internal-combustion engine appeared about 1863 when Jean Joseph Étienne Lenoir constructed a vehicle with a 1-cylinder engine of a type that he had patented in 1860. Lenoir, a French citizen born in Belgium, wrote that his vehicle was clumsy but that its 1½-horsepower motor, making 100 revolutions per minute, had propelled it some six miles in an hour and a half.

Shortly afterward, about 1870, Siegfried Marcus of Vienna built a 4-wheel vehicle having a vertical, 1-cylinder, atmospheric gas engine with electric ignition and a carburetor that used liquid fuel. This automobile is no longer in existence, but it is said to have run satisfactorily.

Marcus' second automobile, said to have been constructed in 1875, but more likely in the 1880s, is preserved at the Technisches Museum für Industrie und Gewerbe in Vienna. It is powered with a horizontal, 1-cylinder, 4-cycle, ¾-horsepower, internal-combustion engine using liquid fuel and electric ignition. The vehicle has four wooden-spoke wheels, is guided by means of a steering wheel, and can accommodate four passengers on two crosswise seats. It is reported that this automobile was operated on the streets of Vienna in the spring of 1950.

Further improvements in gasoline-powered vehicles came in the mid-1880s with the near-simultaneous, though independent, construction in Germany of a 2-wheel machine by Gottlieb Daimler and a 3-wheeler by Karl Benz. Daimler's motorcycle, powered by a 1-cylinder, 4-cycle engine, was the first automotive vehicle produced by the subsequently world-famous Daimler Motoren Gesellschaft, maker of the renowned Mercedes and, later, of the Mercedes-Benz automobiles. Daimler was aided through the years by his friend Wilhelm Maybach.

This gasoline-powered tricycle of 1886 was the first vehicle built by Karl Benz. It had a 1-cylinder engine.

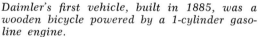

Daimler's first vehicle, built in 1885, was a wooden bicycle powered by a 1-cylinder gasoline engine.

Siegfried Marcus' vehicle of the 1880s probably is the earliest gasoline automobile in existence. It is preserved in the Technisches Museum für Industrie und Gewerbe at Vienna.

A NEW INDUSTRY IN AMERICA

In 1879, an application for a patent covering a vehicle having an internal-combustion engine was submitted by George B. Selden of Rochester, New York. Selden's patent was not issued until 1895 and it had only a short life, but it had great effect on a young American industry. The model that Selden submitted with his application for patent is pictured and described in the following section, devoted to the collection in the Museum of History and Technology.

Charles E. and J. Frank Duryea were notable pioneers of the development of the automobile in America. Their 1-cylinder gasoline automobile of 1893-1894, built in Springfield, Massachusetts, is pictured here and in the section devoted to the Museum's collection, where it is described.

The Duryea Motor Wagon Company's construction of 13 identical automobiles in 1896 was the first instance of mass production of an automobile in America, and the sale of the first of these cars was the first sale of a gasoline-powered automobile in this country. Only one of the original 13 cars remains; it is in the private collection of George H. Waterman of East Greenwich, Rhode Island. A slightly different model, completed in October 1896, won a gold medal in England for finishing first in the London-to-Brighton run on November 14, 1896. The medal is now in the Museum of History and Technology.

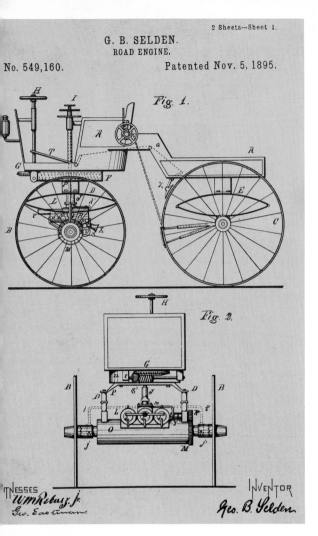

G. B. SELDEN.
ROAD ENGINE.

No. 549,160.

2 Sheets—Sheet 1.

Patented Nov. 5, 1895.

A reproduction of a sheet of Selden's patent that was granted in 1895 for the vehicle he proposed in 1879.

An early photo of the 1893-1894 Duryea gasoline automobile now in the Museum of History and Technology.

Charles E. Duryea in the 2-cylinder, pneumatic-tired Duryea that won the Chicago Times-Herald race on November 28, 1895. His brother Frank drove the car in the race.

Elwood Haynes in his first automobile, built in 1894. The car is now in the Museum of History and Technology.

Charles Brady King at the tiller of his experimental 4-cylinder automobile in 1896 at Detroit.

Elwood Haynes, a metallurgical engineer, worked for several years on the design of a gasoline-powered vehicle. His first car, built in Kokomo, Indiana, made a successful trial trip on July 4, 1894. This automobile, which underwent a change in construction not long after its initial run, is in the collection of the Museum of History and Technology.

The work of Stephen M. Balzer, another pioneer, is represented in the Museum's collection by his first automobile, a small rotary-engined carriage that was built in 1894. This car is the only Balzer-constructed automobile known to exist, but Balzer built other automobiles, and different models appear in the drawings and specifications of several patents that were granted to him in the same period.

In 1893, Charles Brady King, of Detroit, planned a motor tricycle, and in that and the following year he planned several 4-wheel vehicles to be powered with Sintz, 1-cylinder, 2-cycle gasoline engines. These were never built. In 1895 King began constructing an automobile powered by a 4-cylinder, 4-cycle gasoline engine of his own design, and this vehicle, successfully operated on March 6, 1896, is believed to have been the first automobile driven on the streets of Detroit. This car was dismantled shortly after its trial run, and King later gave some of its valves to Henry Ford who used them in the engine of his first vehicle.

Henry Ford, machinist and one-time farmer, experimented with gasoline engines for several years before he built, in his little workshop on Bagley Avenue in Detroit, a 4-wheel, tiller-steered vehicle powered with his own 2-cylinder, 4-cycle, horizontal gasoline engine. This car (now exhibited in the Henry Ford Museum) had its first test run on the streets of Detroit on June 4, 1896, with Charles B. King as a passenger. Later, Ford built several successful racing cars, and in 1903 the newly formed Ford Motor Company offered to the public the first Model A Ford, a 2-cylinder machine.

A 3-wheel, steam-propelled passenger vehicle, designed by Ransom E. Olds, was constructed in Lansing, Michigan, in 1886. This steamer, later rebuilt as a 4-wheeler, was shipped to a purchaser in Bombay, India, in 1893. Olds' first gasoline automobile, built in late 1895 or early in 1896, was destroyed by fire, but the Museum of History and Technology has one of four similar automobiles built by Olds in 1897. The Museum's automobile is the oldest surviving Olds vehicle.

A few other makes and types of automobiles were constructed in this country before the close of the century, and many experimental machines were designed and built in this period and in the early 1900s. Among such vehicles were steam-, electric-, and gasoline-powered automobiles, and many

Henry Ford's first automobile, his 2-cylinder machine of 1896, is preserved in the Henry Ford Museum.

Stephen M. Balzer in one of his experimental, rotary-engine vehicles.

of these led to the development of successful enterprises, some of which are still in business.

The first transcontinental automobile trip was made in 1903 when H. Nelson Jackson drove his 2-cylinder Winton from San Francisco to New York in 63 days. This car is in the Museum's collection. One month after the Winton's successful trip, Tom Fetch, driving a 1-cylinder Packard, made the same journey in a few days less time. Shortly afterward, L. L. Whitman and E. T. Hammond made the same trip in about ten weeks in a 1-cylinder Oldsmobile.

As time passed, the automobile became more and more reliable. Manufacturing methods were improved and service facilities became increasingly available. Garages hired mechanics and stocked replacement parts, and the brawny hand of the blacksmith was laid less often on the machine needing repairs. As the risk of breakdowns lessened, more and more women began to drive.

Assembly-line manufacture, which is based on interchangeability of parts, made possible the high production records that the automobile industry has achieved in times of both peace and war. The importance of the interchangeability of parts was demonstrated as early as 1908 when the Royal Automobile Club of Great Britain presented the Sir Thomas Dewar trophy to Cadillac for the most meritorious performance in any trial held by the Club during the year. The trial consisted of completely disassembling three new 1-cylinder Cadillac automobiles,

H. Nelson Jackson and Sewall K. Crocker in Jackson's 1903 Winton, the first automobile to be driven across the United States. The car is in the Museum of History and Technology.

Scene in the Duryea factory at Springfield, Massachusetts, during the assembling of some of the 13 identical cars the company "mass-produced" in 1896.

mixing all the parts, and reassembling the vehicles from parts picked at random. After the cars were reassembled, the engines were started easily and the automobiles made 500-mile test runs. This trial showed that parts manufactured within certain tolerances permitted faster and more economical assembly than parts produced by hand fitting; in addition, it showed that the production of interchangeable parts was a workable American system.

Since November 28, 1895, the date of America's first automobile race, many speed contests and reliability trials have been held, and both types of events have had great effect on the development of the automobile. These competitive events spurred manufacturers and engineers to develop better and better tires, alloys, lubricants, and other components of the automobile. The result has been that our cars have become more serviceable and last longer.

**The Collection
of Automobiles
and Motorcycles
in the Museum
of History
and Technology**

Roper Steam Velocipede

about 1869
Gift of John H. Bacon in 1956

The oldest self-propelled road vehicle in the Museum's collection is the steam-powered velocipede built in the late 1860s by Sylvester H. Roper of Roxbury, Massachusetts.

At first glance the machine appears to be a converted velocipede, but examination reveals that its frame was forged expressly for this self-powered vehicle.

The two 34-inch-diameter wooden-spoke wheels have wooden felloes and iron-band tires. The front wheel is supported in a

The steam velocipede built by Sylvester H. Roper about 1869. Only one older self-propelled road vehicle, the Dudgeon steamer, is known to exist in America. Photo above shows arrangement of cylinders, valve chests, and the feed-water pump on the left cylinder.

forged wrought-iron fork having a straight handlebar with wooden grips. Footrests are provided at the bottom of the fork. The wheelbase is 49 inches.

A vertical, fire-tube boiler is suspended between the wheels, and a chimney angles back from the top of the boiler housing. The lower half of the housing served as the firebox (the grate of which is missing). Charcoal was fed through a small circular door on the left side of the firebox. The housing is suspended from the center of the frame by means of a spring-loaded hanger (intended to absorb some of the road shock) and is braced at the bottom by two stay rods connected to the rear of the frame.

A hand-operated water pump is mounted vertically on the left forward side of the boiler housing. Three water-level cocks are located nearby, and there is a drain valve at the left rear of the boiler's base.

Oscillating steam cylinders are pivoted on each side of the frame, next to the chimney. From outside measurements, it is estimated that the bore of the cylinders is about two and one-quarter inches. The piston rods worked on 2½-inch cranks on the ends of the rear axle. Piston valves for the cylinders were operated by eccentrics adjacent to their cranks, and a feed-water pump was operated by the left-cylinder crank. The exhaust steam, carried by tubing into the base of the chimney, provided forced draft. Apparently, while the machine was at rest a forced draft was provided by a tiny steam pipe that leads from the safety valve at the top rear of the boiler to the base of the chimney. There is a damper valve within the chimney.

The throttle, located at the top front of the boiler housing, was actuated by forward twisting of the handlebar. A friction brake was applied against the rim of the front wheel when the handlebar was twisted toward the driver. Heavy tubing leads from the throttle to the steam chests of the cylinders, and other tubing leads from the boiler to a steam gauge at the front of the frame.

The water supply for the boiler was contained in a tank that also served as the saddle. The filler opening is at the front of the tank. Water was supplied to the hand pump and the feed-water pump by means of tubing that leads from the bottom of the tank.

It is clear that the builder of this early self-propelled vehicle was an ingenious as well as an accomplished machinist.

Model of Selden Automobile

1879
Transferred from the United States Patent Office in 1908

George B. Selden, a patent attorney and inventor in Rochester, New York, submitted this model to the United States Patent Office on May 8, 1879, when he filed application for a patent on a road vehicle powered by an internal-combustion engine. Selden's patent, number 549160, was not issued until November 5, 1895.

Many pioneer American automobile manufacturers and importers were licensed under Selden's patent, but others contested its validity. On November 4, 1899, just four years after the patent was issued, Selden made a contract with the Electric Vehicle Company, manufacturer of Columbia electric automobiles at Hartford, Connecticut. Subsequently, on March 5, 1903, the Association of Licensed Automobile Manufacturers was

Patent plate of the type affixed to automobiles manufactured under the Selden license. The serial number is in the lower left corner.

Model of automobile that George B. Selden submitted to the Patent Office along with his patent application of 1879.

formed, with the Electric Vehicle Company and the Winton Motor-Carriage Company among its ten charter members. The licensed companies agreed to pay a royalty of one and one-quarter percent of the retail list price on all cars sold. The royalty was cut later to one percent, and finally to four-fifths of one percent. Each automobile built by a licensed manufacturer carried a patent plate.

The association published annual illustrated handbooks containing specifications of the various makes of cars produced by the member manufacturers. At its height, the association's membership comprised 87 percent of the automobile manufacturers in this country and produced over 90 percent of the gasoline automobiles built. The best-known independent was Henry Ford, who refused to join the association. In a suit filed

George B. Selden and Henry R. Selden (standing) with the Selden automobile constructed in 1904. This contemporary photograph was taken in front of the garage of Wyckoff, Church, and Partridge, automobile dealers, at Broadway and West 56th Street in New York.

against Ford on October 21, 1903, the court sustained the patent, holding that three of the claims were valid and infringed. Ford put up a bond and appealed. The issue, popularly known as the Selden patent suit, finally was decided in the Court of Appeals in January 1911 when the claims of the patent were held to be valid only in cases involving the use of engines of the Brayton type; hence, the patent was held not to have been infringed because the Brayton engine was not being used then by anyone. The Association of Licensed Automobile Manufacturers was dissolved shortly thereafter.

In addition to its licensing activities, the association had carried on research and standardization work under its mechanical branch. About a year prior to the final court decision, the mechanical branch had been discontinued and its records, apparatus, and engineering library turned over to the Society of Automotive Engineers. Since that time this society has been instrumental in standardizing measurements pertaining to the automobile.

Selden's patent application described an automobile with an engine of six cylinders—three compression cylinders, and three power cylinders that were to be fed a mixture of air and liquid hydrocarbon—and with a compressed air tank, clutch, foot brake, muffler, front-wheel drive, and a power shaft arranged so that it would run faster than the propelling wheels. In 1904

Hugo Gibson at the wheel of the 1904 Selden car at a Guttenberg, New Jersey, racetrack in June 1907.

a full-size Selden vehicle was constructed under the direction of Henry R. Selden and George B. Selden, Jr., sons of the inventor, as an exhibit for the court hearing the patent suit. The original engine, built in 1877, was used. The 1904 vehicle (illustrated here) is now in the Long Island Automotive Museum at Southampton, New York.

The front-wheel assembly of the 1904 Selden could be rotated completely—a steering arrangement that also provided reverse. Photo at right shows the front of the car; the one at left shows the front-wheel assembly after it has been rotated 90 degrees, with the rear of the engine now at vehicle's right side.

Long Steam Tricycle

about 1880
Gift of John H. Bacon in 1956

The oldest completely operable self-propelled road vehicle on display in the Museum is a steam tricycle built about 1880 by George A. Long of Northfield, Massachusetts. After a period of disuse following its construction, Long's original tricycle was disassembled and its parts scattered. In 1946, however, the donor of the vehicle obtained the engine, along with its feed-water pump and driving pulleys, from the 96-year-old builder who then was living in Boston. At that time Long recalled that many years earlier he had seen other parts of the machine in

The 2-cylinder, V-type steam engine on Long's tricycle.

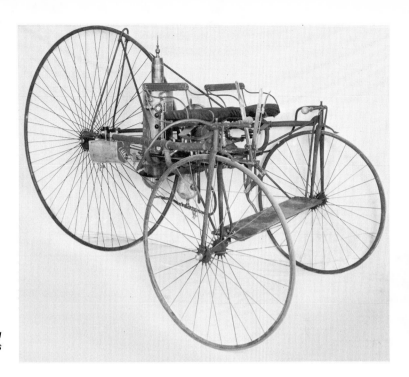

The steam tricycle built by George A. Long about 1880 is still operable, but some of its parts are modern replacements.

Northfield. A search by Mr. Bacon resulted in his obtaining most of the missing parts and, subsequently, to the machine's restoration, which involved the use of some replacement parts.

George Eli Whitney of Bridgeport, Connecticut, constructed the replacement fire-tube boiler and its appurtenances, and Russell Davis of Leominster, Massachusetts, performed other important work in the tricycle's restoration. Whitney is well known as a designer and builder of pioneer steam automobiles in the mid-1890s, and his work greatly influenced the Stanley brothers of later steam fame.

Long designed and built the tricycle's engine at Northfield in 1879, and a year or so later he constructed the framework and running gear in Albert A. Pope's Columbia bicycle plant located in the factory of the Weed Sewing Machine Company at Hartford, Connecticut.

On August 29, 1882, Long applied for a patent on a "steam road-vehicle" consisting of a two-seated, self-propelled tricycle powered by a 2-cylinder steam engine using gasoline as fuel. He was granted the patent, number 281091, on July 10, 1883. Drawings on the patent papers reveal a tricycle that closely resembles the Museum's restored vehicle. Interestingly, gasoline was specified as the fuel.

Long wanted to provide the front-wheel forks with improved steering heads that used small balls, such as those that appeared later on the steering heads of bicycles and motorcycles.

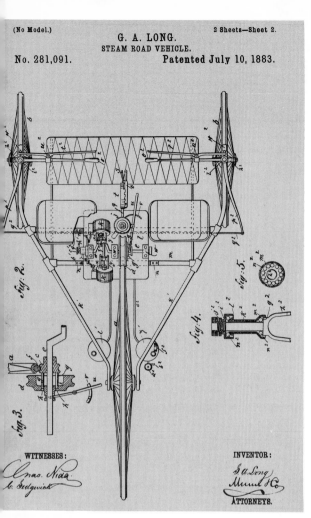

Fig. 2.

Fig. 3.

Fig. 4.

Fig. 5.

WITNESSES:

Chas. Nida.
Le Sedgwick

INVENTOR:

G. A. Long
Munn & Co.
ATTORNEYS.

Reproduction of a sheet from the patent granted to George A. Long in 1883 for the steam tricycle he proposed the previous year.

At the time he constructed his tricycle, however, Long was unable to make such small balls, so he equipped the two steering heads with plain bushings.

The rear wheel, five feet in diameter, is the driving wheel. The two front wheels, three feet in diameter, are mounted in steering forks whose heads are connected by a curved tie rod. Spoon brakes operate against each of the solid tires on the front wheels. The design of the steering and braking systems indicates that Long intended that the machine would be operated by two persons. A single driver would have difficulty in steering only one of the handlebars and in operating both brake levers. Each seat is mounted on a full-elliptic spring, and its height is adjustable.

The 2-cylinder, 90-degree, V-type engine has a stroke of one and five-eighths inches. It is attached to a steel plate mounted in the framework on small rollers so that it can be moved backwards and forwards by means of a lever pivoted in front of the seats. There are two pulleys on the crankshaft. The larger pulley is splined and can move lengthwise on the shaft. When the engine plate is brought backward, one of the driving pulleys is brought into contact with the tire of the rear wheel. As the pulleys have different diameters, two driving ratios are provided. The boiler and one of the two water tanks also are mounted on the engine plate, an arrangement which requires that the tube between the fuel tank and the burner (beneath the boiler) and the one between the two water tanks be of the flexible type.

The vehicle's replaced parts include the boiler, burner, engine mounting plate, fuel and water tanks, all gauges and piping, the hand-operated air pump, and the water pump, which is from an early steam automobile.

The restored tricycle, weighing about 350 pounds, operates at a steam pressure of approximately 100 pounds per square inch.

Duryea

1893-1894
Gift of Inglis M. Uppercu in 1920

This automobile, built by Charles E. and J. Frank Duryea, had a friction drive when it was first operated on the streets of Springfield, Massachusetts, in September 1893. A few months later, in January 1894, the Duryeas operated the car with the present gear transmission.

The 1-cylinder, 4-cycle, 4-horsepower, water-cooled gasoline engine, with make-and-break electric ignition, lies almost horizontally beneath the carriage body, and its cylinder head extends backward above the rear axle. The engine, transmission, and differential are mounted in a frame supported by the two axles. The water tank is to the right of the engine.

Bevel gears transmitted power from the vertical crankshaft

Two views of the Museum's 1893-1894 Duryea automobile as it appears today. The car was restored in 1958.

to a main horizontal shaft, and then spur gears transmitted it to a small jackshaft having a small double-shrouded pinion at each end. The differential is built into this jackshaft, and a combination sprocket and internal gear hangs from each pinion. Chains connect the jackshaft sprockets with large sprockets attached to the inside of the wooden spokes of the carriage-type rear wheels, which have iron tires 44½ inches in diameter.

Three friction clutches on the main shaft—two for the forward speeds and one for reverse—are operated through cable connections by an up-or-down movement of the steering tiller. The pivot axis of each of the C-type steering knuckles on the front wheels intercepts the plane of its wheel at the ground. The front wheels are similar to the rear ones except that they have smaller diameters, 38½ inches.

The hand-starting crank, which projects at the rear of the car, turned the crankshaft by means of a pair of bevel gears that automatically unmeshed when the engine started. A floatless, constant-level jet carburetor received gasoline from a supply tank above the carburetor and to the left of the engine. A needle valve regulated the flow of fuel to produce the desired power and engine speed. At slower engine speeds, the excess fuel overflowed into a tank below the carburetor; it then was returned to the main supply tank by action of a hand pump. A projection on the piston head actuated the electric make-and-break ignition system.

Despite its age, this car was basically complete when it came to the Smithsonian in 1920. When it was restored in the Museum's shop in 1958 only the lamps, jackshaft sprockets, chains, and a few minor parts had to be replaced.

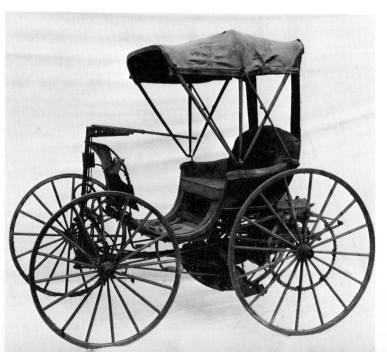

A photo of the Museum's 1893-1894 Duryea automobile taken soon after the Smithsonian received the car in 1920.

Haynes

1894
Gift of Elwood Haynes in 1910.

This car, designed by Elwood Haynes, was constructed in the shop of Elmer and Edgar Apperson at Kokomo, Indiana, in the fall of 1893 and the spring of 1894. On July 4, 1894, it made a successful trial trip at a speed of about seven miles an hour.

Although this is the original Haynes automobile, its construction is somewhat different than at the time of its first successful trip. About two years after the trial run, the original 1-horsepower, 2-cycle, Sintz gasoline engine was replaced by a 2-horsepower one; the 28-inch, cushion-tire, wire-spoke wheels were replaced with ones having single-tube pneumatic tires 36 inches in outside diameter; and the worm-and-gear-driven, swinging front axle of carriage design was fixed in place and pivoted steering knuckles were fitted to its ends. The new steering mechanism was operated by means of a tiller.

The vertical, 1-cylinder, water-cooled engine, with make-and-break ignition, delivered power by chain to a jackshaft forward of the motor and parallel to the rear axle. At each end of this jackshaft is a small sprocket that is connected by a chain to a larger sprocket on each rear wheel, and at the left end of the jackshaft is a spring-loaded, friction-type differential. Two friction clutches on the jackshaft offered a choice of two forward speeds. They were operated by means of a chain actuated by a sprocket on the lower end of a vertical T-rod in reach of the driver. A third forward speed of very low ratio was provided by a clutch-and-sprocket device on the right end of the rear axle, but the car no longer has a mechanism for operating this device. No reverse gear was provided. The engine was started by means of a removable crank that was inserted between the spokes of the right rear wheel. A brake lever operated a friction band on the end of the jackshaft.

The water tank, under the seat, is connected to the engine by two rubber hoses. The gasoline tank is beneath the floor, below the level of the carburetor, and there is an accelerator pedal. A mechanical pump, operated by the ignition linkage, sent the fuel to the carburetor, and another pump, operated by the same linkage, circulated the cooling water.

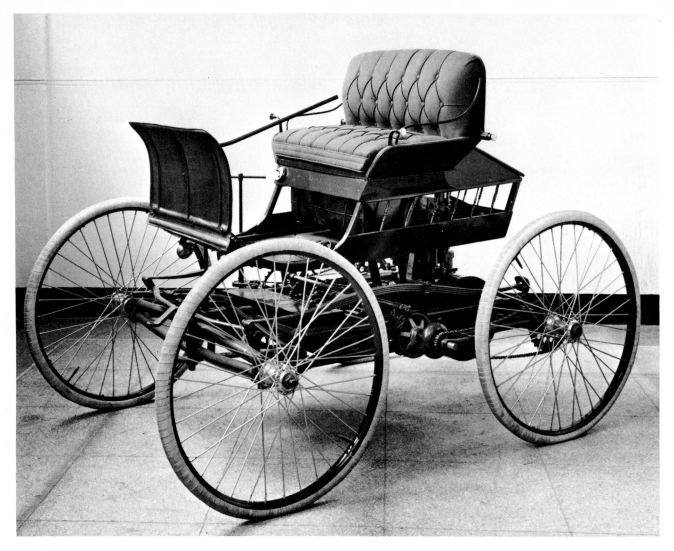

The Museum's 1894 Haynes automobile as it appears today. A photo on page 19 shows the car as originally constructed.

The rectangular frame is of tubular construction; the body rides on a pair of long side-springs; and the vehicle weighs about 1,000 pounds.

The car was restored by the Museum's shop in 1961. At that time the original tires, which were badly deteriorated, were replaced with a new set made by Gehrig Tire Company, following the pattern of the originals.

Balzer

1894
Gift of Stephen M. Balzer in 1899

The 1894 Balzer is a unique automobile. It is less than six feet long and three feet wide, and the diameter of the front wheels is ten inches less than that of the rear ones. The front wheels, carrying 20-inch tires, are mounted in bicycle-type forks that are connected by a tie rod and steered by a tiller.

When the 3-cylinder, air-cooled, rotary-type engine was running, the cylinders and crankcase revolved in a vertical plane around the stationary crankshaft. A stub shaft, turning with the crankcase, carried the driving gears of a 3-step, constant-mesh transmission that provides three forward speeds but no reverse. The driven shaft of the transmission is geared to a clutch on the divided rear axle at the propelling, left rear wheel.

The driver selected the desired gear ratio by operating a

Rear view of the 1894 Balzer automobile.

The 1894 Balzer automobile.

lever (at his right) that keyed the appropriate driven gear to its shaft. The same lever also controlled the clutch.

A brush-wiped commutator on the driving shaft distributed current to the make-and-break ignition system of the cylinders. Each cylinder has two poppet valves—an inlet valve of the automatic type that opened by atmospheric pressure when the piston was on its suction stroke, and an exhaust valve operated by a cam (located on the stationary crankshaft and driven by gearing connected to the revolving crankcase) that revolved at the required speed on the crankshaft. The make-and-break linkage was operated by the same cam that controlled the exhaust valve

Gasoline vapor was piped from a tank, beneath the floorboard, through a fitting (now incomplete) which may have been a mixing valve. The mixture traveled through a hollow shaft to a connection with three pipes within a heating chamber built on the rotating crankcase; it then passed through these pipes to the inlet valves. The exhaust gases left the cylinders through three other pipes leading into the chamber on the crankcase. This chamber, which has many small holes drilled through its outer wall, could have served as a muffler as well as a stove to heat the incoming mixture.

When the vehicle was restored by the Museum's shop in 1959 its badly deteriorated tires were replaced with single-tube pneumatic ones. Originally, each of the front tires had a short opening into which a two-ended, sausage-like inner tube had been inserted and the opening had been laced closed as in a football. The original rear tires were similar to conventional open casings except that they had a wire, tightened by a turnbuckle, inside each bead.

Clarke Gasoline Tricycle

1897
Gift of Louis S. Clarke in 1947

In 1897, Louis S. Clarke of Pittsburgh, Pennsylvania, founded the Pittsburgh Motor Vehicle Company, with himself as president and engineer, and constructed this experimental motor tricycle. With the experience thus gained, in the following year the company built a 4-wheel automobile, which is now in the Henry Ford Museum. The name of Clarke's firm was changed in 1899 to the Autocar Company—one of the few pioneer automobile companies surviving today.

Louis S. Clarke with his first Autocar. The tricycle was about 48 years old when this photo was taken in 1944. (Autocar Company photo.)

Rear view of the 1897 Clarke tricycle, showing detail of the 1-cylinder gasoline engine.

The Museum's 1897 Clarke tricycle was the first vehicle built by Louis S. Clarke, founder of the Autocar Company.

Clarke's 1897 vehicle, which is known as the first Autocar, is a conventional tricycle equipped with a gasoline engine that drives the rear wheels. The frame consists of standard bicycle parts and some special parts designed and made by Clarke. The 1-cylinder engine has a mechanically operated exhaust valve and an automatic intake valve. On its crankshaft extension is a gear that meshes directly with the ring gear of the differential. No gear changes are provided. A single lever operates both the clutch (located on the crankshaft extension between the engine and the driving gear) and a band brake on the drum of the clutch.

There is no throttle, but the engine speed could be varied by means of a spark-advance lever, and there is a fuel-flow regulator on the exhaust-heated, gasoline vaporizer. The main exhaust pipe leads into a small muffler. The gasoline tank is in the frame beneath the saddle, and the batteries and high-tension coil are in a box farther forward in the frame.

Bicycle pedals, with the usual sprockets and chain, enabled the rider to start the engine and, in event of a breakdown, to propel the vehicle. An overrunning clutch is built into this gearing so that the pedals are not driven by the engine while the tricycle is in motion. The front wheel is supported in a steering fork equipped with handlebars.

The wire-spoke, bicycle-type wheels carry 26-by-2½-inch single-tube pneumatic tires, and Clarke has stated that the tire on the front wheel is an original.

The tricycle was restored in 1963 by Dale C. Price of Cambridge, Maryland. Some of the original parts have been replaced —the saddle, handlebar grips, spark plug, rear tires, and a relief pipe and valve on the engine's crankcase.

Olds

1897

Gift of Olds Motor Works in 1915

The Museum's 1897 Olds is the only remaining example of the first five gasoline automobiles built by Ransom E. Olds, who produced one such car in 1895 or 1896 and four more of the same design in 1897.

Ransom E. Olds built his first gasoline automobile in 1895 or 1896, and in 1897 at Lansing, Michigan, the newly formed Olds Motor Vehicle Company, of which he was manager, constructed four other cars of the same design. The Museum's automobile, one of the four, is the only remaining example of the earliest Olds vehicles. It carried four passengers at ten miles an hour when it was first operated in 1897.

The car's 6-horsepower, 1-cylinder, water-cooled engine is

The rear-mounted 1-cylinder engine of the 1897 Olds.

placed horizontally beneath the body, toward the rear. The vertical flywheel is located in the center, so that the transverse crankshaft lies about midway between the front and rear axles.

Three friction clutches, mounted on extensions of the crankshaft on both sides of the flywheel, provide two forward speeds and a reverse. Each of the forward-speed clutches, mounted on the left side, engages a chain sprocket on the crankshaft; the reverse clutch, mounted on the right side, operates in conjunction with a planetary gear. The three clutches are controlled by a system of cams and levers at the lower end of a vertical post on the driver's right. Chains transmitted power to sprockets on a sleeve on the live rear axle. The sleeve is integral with the driving element of the differential. A spring compensator for absorbing shocks of power transmission is built into the differential, and a band brake on the differential unit is operated by a pedal.

The cylinder end of the engine is attached rigidly to the rear-axle support, while the crankshaft end is supported by curved iron straps attached to the front axle. The body rests on three full-elliptic springs—a transverse one at the front axle and the other two at the rear. The driver steered by operating a tiller that swings the front wheels on their vertical pivots. The wooden, artillery-type wheels are equipped with solid rubber tires. The front wheels are 32 inches in diameter; the rear ones, 36 inches.

The radiator consists of 21 long horizontal tubes that are mounted flat against the underside of the body and run fore and aft. Two rubber hoses connect the radiator to the water tank and to the water jacket of the cylinder.

The gasoline tank is suspended beneath the engine. A small pump, driven by an eccentric arm on the crankshaft, forced the fuel from the tank to the carburetor. The eccentric arm also operated the exhaust valve of the engine and controlled the make-and-break electric ignition. The spring-closed intake valve is of the automatic type.

Winton

1898

Gift of Winton Engine Company in 1929

This car, built by Alexander Winton in 1898, was the first Winton automobile to be sold by the Winton Motor-Carriage Company, of Cleveland, Ohio. It also was the first car built of a group of about 25 such automobiles the company scheduled for production in one year. Robert Allison, a 70-year-old resident of Port Carbon, Pennsylvania, purchased the car on March 24, 1898; later, the Winton Company bought it back from him. Several earlier experimental models were constructed but never sold.

Power was supplied by a 1-cylinder, water-cooled, horizontal gasoline engine with make-and-break ignition. The transmission is connected by a chain to a small shaft (situated directly above the rear-axle housing) that is geared directly to a differential unit on the rear axle. This shaft also carries a brake drum with a contracting band actuated by a left-foot pedal.

The transmission consists of three exposed pairs of constant-mesh gears on two transverse parallel shafts. The rear shaft is a right-hand extension of the crankshaft. The gearing of the left pair of gears on the crankshaft is integral with the driving sprocket of the chain. The right pair has a reverse idler gear in its train.

The two forward speeds and the reverse are controlled by two levers at the driver's right and by a small knob. To engage the low-speed gear, the driver turned the knob so that the mating and otherwise free-running gear was clutched to the front shaft; he then pulled the left lever, causing the middle gear to clutch to the crankshaft. Thus, the motion of the crankshaft was transmitted to the front shaft and back to the sprocket gear running free on the crankshaft. To engage the high-speed gear, the driver pulled the right lever, causing the driving sprocket to clutch directly to the crankshaft. The driver put the car in reverse by pushing the left lever; this action caused the right-hand gear to clutch to the front shaft and transmit the crankshaft's motion through the reverse idler gear and the front shaft back to the free-running sprocket on the crankshaft.

The accelerator pedal originally was connected to a carbu-

This 1898 automobile was the first Winton car sold.

retor (now missing) at the rear of the engine. A large fin-cooled water tank is suspended under the body at the right rear, and the gasoline tank is above and to the left of the engine. The engine was started through use of a hand crank (normally stored in a floorboard receptacle) that was fitted through a hole in the body and into the gearing on the right side of the engine.

The front axle, which has steering knuckles at each end, was steered by tiller. Reach-rods that connect the front axle and the housing of the rear axle kept the two axles parallel. The car's frame rests on four full-elliptic springs mounted on the axles, and it supports the engine. This was one of the earliest instances in which the engine was mounted on a spring-supported chassis.

The wire-spoke wheels have 34-by-3-inch single-tube pneumatic tires in the front and 36-by-3-inch ones in the rear. The top and upholstery were replaced in 1957 by the National Auto Top Company of Washington, D. C.

Knox

1899

Lent by Mrs. Lansing Van Auken in 1924

This automobile, built in 1899 by Harry A. Knox of Springfield, Massachusetts, is an example of one of the many makes of 3-wheelers that appeared around the turn of the century. When it paraded in the Hudson-Fulton celebration in New York in 1909, this car won a prize of $25 for being the oldest machine to cover the line of march under its own power.

The chassis is characterized by simplicity of construction, which was one of Knox's objectives in designing a 3-wheel automobile. The two sides of the roughly triangular frame are parallel at the rear for half their length, begin to converge at a center cross member, and sweep upward at the front to a motorcycle-type fork in the apex of the triangle. The front wheel is steered by a tiller that is pivoted to the upper end of the fork so that it can be moved away from the driver. The rear of the frame is bolted directly to the bearing housings of the rear-axle shafts. Shock-absorption between the chassis and the body is provided by three full-elliptic springs, one at each side in the rear and one mounted transversely at the front just behind the fork.

The driving sprocket of a bevel-gear differential (at the hub of the left wheel) is attached to the inner end of the left wheel's short tubular shaft. The right wheel's axle shaft passes through this tubular shaft. The wire-spoke wheels have single-tube, 28-by-2½-inch tires. A small mudguard, mounted behind the front wheel, turns with the fork.

The 1-cylinder, 8-horsepower engine, with 4½-inch bore and 6-inch stroke, is air cooled by radiation from many small rods that project from the cylinder. It is mounted horizontally in the center of the car, with its crankshaft parallel to the ground and its cylinder to the rear. It is supported by two metal hangers, one attached to the chassis at the rear and the other to the center cross member.

A small eccentric, at the right end of the crankshaft, drove a pushrod connected to a piston-shaped valve in the valve chamber. A cam, driven at half the crankshaft speed, operated another pushrod which, in turn, actuated a poppet valve between the combustion chamber and the piston valve. The poppet valve, which remained open for almost the complete turn of the crankshaft, served as both exhaust and intake valve. The position of the piston valve determined whether the exhaust or intake manifold was to function. The spark plug is at the rear of the cylinder. The original spark plug and all the ball bearings were made in the Knox factory.

The ignition timer is mounted adjacent to the engine camshaft. The portion of the camshaft that drove the cam of the timer is spirally splined, and it was free to slide with respect to the rotor, advancing or retarding the ignition as it did so. The 3-dimensional cam is integral with the splined shaft, and as it was moved back and forth with respect to its follower it advanced or retarded the motion of the follower; consequently, it regulated the valve timing and thus controlled the speed of the engine.

The carburetor is mounted on the back of the frame next to the intake end of the piston valve. It is of the constant-level type, with a hinged float, and its horizontal needle valve is near the top of the bowl; thus, it is similar to and has several of the essential features of the modern-type carburetor. A fuel jet, adjusted by a metering pin, projects into the intake manifold and then leads directly to the intake end of the piston valve. The side of the manifold opposite the jet is perforated with many small holes through which air was sucked as the piston descended. The air was carried past the jet to form an explosive mixture that passed by the piston valve and then the poppet valve. There is no butterfly control for the carburetor. Engine speed was controlled only by the sliding camshaft. A long tube connects the exhaust end of the piston valve to the muffler, which is transversely mounted next to the chassis cross member in front of the engine.

To start the engine, the operator first placed a rubber hose on a vent tube mounted on the carburetor's cover plate and leading to the float chamber. He then blew into the hose, forcing the fuel mixture from the jet into the intake manifold.

Oil from a cylindrical, sight-glass tank (bolted to the front of the crankcase) flowed through two lines to each of the two main bearings and then dripped into the crankcase. Bleeder holes in the oil-ring groove of the piston prevented "oil pumping" and returned the oil to the crankcase.

The flywheel is on the left end of the crankshaft. The planetary transmission provides two speeds forward and neutral. There is no reverse. The driver controlled the transmission by means of a vertical shaft mounted to the left of the seat. The same shaft also supports the shaft that controlled the engine speed. A chain connects the transmission sprocket to the sprocket on the rear axle. The gas tank, battery, and coil are

The Kelsey and Tilney experimental 1-cylinder automobile, built in 1899.

located beneath the seat, and the back part of the body provides a utility compartment that has a wooden cover. Two leather rebound straps pass beneath the chassis at the rear. An ignition switch is located on the front of the coil compartment, behind the black leather seat curtain, and near the left edge of the floorboard is a ratchet-held brake pedal that operated a band on a drum of the transmission. A warning bell is mounted to the right of the pedal.

The Museum's 1899 Knox automobile. Harry A. Knox built several cars of this type around 1900.

Kelsey and Tilney

1899
Gift of Joseph R. Darling in 1923

Carl W. Kelsey and I. Sheldon Tilney built this experimental automobile in 1899 at Chestnut Hill, Pennsylvania, but never put it into production. In later years, however, Kelsey produced 3-wheel and 4-wheel cars of different design.

The pipe frame supports a light, 2-passenger body mounted on three full-elliptic springs. The three wire-spoke wheels are 25 inches in diameter and used single-tube pneumatic tires. The front wheels are steered by a tiller; the single rear wheel is the driving wheel.

The engine is supported horizontally on the left side of the frame, with its crankshaft end toward the rear. A planetary transmission, providing two forward speeds and reverse, is assembled on a transverse jackshaft driven by sprockets and chain from the engine. The drive to the rear-wheel sprocket is transmitted by chain from a sprocket on the jackshaft. The driver controlled the high-speed clutch by means of a lever near his right knee, and operated the low-speed and reverse gears by pedals.

The 1-cylinder, 4-cycle engine, cooled by the circulation of water stored in a tank in the upper right part of the body, has an intake valve of the automatic type, an exhaust valve operated by a cam that was driven by gears at half the crankshaft speed, and a muffler. A gasoline vaporizer (above the intake valve) was fed by gravity from a small tank behind the seat. Originally, the ignition was of the make-and-break type, but the car later was equipped with high-tension coil and spark plug. The operator advanced and retarded the spark by means of a small lever to the right of the seat cushion.

Locomobile Steam Automobile

1900

Gift of Mrs. H. H. Smith in 1929

This unidentified engine, given to the Museum by Louis S. Clarke in 1922, is quite similar to the one in the Museum's 1900 Locomobile steamer.

The Stanley twins in their first steam automobile, built in 1897.

F. E. and F. O. Stanley, twin brothers, sold their newly created steam-automobile business in 1899 to a group which—first in Newton, Massachusetts, and later in Bridgeport, Connecticut— manufactured the Locomobile car.

The Museum's Locomobile, designated as "Style 2," is car number 2795 and carries a maker's plate bearing the patent date of November 14, 1899. One of the early products of the Bridgeport factory, this car was sold new on July 4, 1900, for $750.

The wooden body rests on three full-elliptic springs—one on each side in the rear and a transverse one at the front. The springs are supported on a light underframe consisting of two longitudinal tubes that are brazed and bolted, at each end, to curved cross tubes, which, in turn, are brazed to two straight cross tubes. The straight cross tube at the rear is divided at its

The Museum's 1900 Locomobile, a steam automobile built by a firm that bought the Stanley brothers' business in 1899.

center to receive the differential gear, which is mounted on the rear axle. Stay tubes and rods on the underframe provide additional rigidity.

The car's tread is 53 inches; its wheelbase, 58 inches. The cycle-type wheels have tangent spokes and steel rims and carry 28-by-2½-inch, single-tube, pneumatic tires.

All principal parts of the driving mechanism are attached to the body. The boiler and engine are below the seat portion of the body; the feed-water tank is below the rear portion.

At the driver's right are three levers that controlled the engine and burner. The driver steered the pivoted front wheels by operating a side bar. The rear wheels are keyed at the ends of the divided rear axle. Power from a 16-tooth sprocket on the crankshaft was transmitted by a chain to a 40-tooth sprocket

The engine of the first Stanley steam automobile, 1897, has a 2½-inch bore and a 4-inch stroke. It was built for the Stanley brothers by the Mason Regulator Company, of Boston, who gave it to the Museum in 1932.

on the differential gear. The driver operated a pedal to contract the brake band of a drum on the sprocket of the differential unit.

The vertical, fire-tube-type boiler is a cylindrical drum consisting of upper and lower tube plates and a shell plate. The tube plates are connected by about 300 copper fire tubes, and the shell plate is strengthened by windings of steel piano wire. The boiler's heating surface, totaling about 30 square feet, consists of about 100 square inches of tube plate and over 4,000 square inches of tube surface. The burner is in a fire box located below the lower tube plate. The smoke box and drum of the boiler are lagged thickly with asbestos.

Water for the boiler flowed from the bottom of a 15-gallon, horseshoe-shaped tank to a feed pump (attached to the engine frame and operated by a rocking lever from one of the engine's crossheads) and then entered the boiler at the lower tube plate. On the right side of the carriage body is a water-level gauge glass that the driver could see readily by glancing in a small mirror near the brake pedal. Also near this pedal is a pressure gauge which indicates that the boiler normally was worked at 150 pounds pressure. Gasoline was fed, by air pressure, to the burner from a cylindrical tank suspended from the frame below the floorboard. The air pressure was indicated by another floorboard gauge.

Each of the vertical engine's two double-acting cylinders has a 2½-inch bore and a 3½-inch stroke. The cranks are set at 90 degrees to each other. Cylinders and steam chest are lagged thickly with asbestos. The engine's normal speed was about 400 revolutions per minute. With a cutoff giving a mean pressure of about 50 pounds, it developed about three brake horsepower; but with no cutoff and with maximum steam pressure it could develop about 10 to 12 brake horsepower for short periods. Thus, since the car weighs only about 700 pounds, the ratio of horsepower to weight was fairly high for that day. Because of the favorable horsepower-to-weight ratio, the early steam cars generally could outperform the heavier, gasoline-powered vehicles for short spurts.

The Locomobile was restored in 1961 by Dale C. Price of Cambridge, Maryland.

Engine of the Stanley steam racing car that established a world's land-speed record—127.659 miles an hour—at Daytona Beach on January 26, 1906. It has a 4½-inch bore and a 6½-inch stroke. Fred Marriott, who drove the car for the speed record, presented the engine to the Smithsonian in 1940.

Riker Electric Automobile

about 1900

Gift of Mrs. Herbert Wadsworth in 1932

At the beginning of the 20th century, the electric motor was better developed than the gasoline engine; consequently, electric automobiles were quieter, cleaner, and more dependable than the early gasoline-powered cars. Such attributes led to the construction of luxurious, closed electric cars, such as this Riker, several years before closed bodies appeared generally on gasoline automobiles.

The Museum's electric automobile of about 1900 was built by the Riker Motor Vehicle Company, of Elizabethport, New Jersey. The tubular front and rear axles are connected by tubular side members, and the frame is strengthened by short tubular diagonal members. The four wheels are of the artillery type, having wooden spokes and felloes. The tires are of solid rubber. The front wheels, 30 inches in diameter, are mounted on pivoted steering knuckles connected by a tubular tie rod. No size is indicated on the front tires; their outside diameter is now about 34 inches, but some wear, of course, has occurred. The rear wheels, 36 inches in diameter, have tires that are marked 42 by 3½ but that actually measure 41 inches in outside diameter. The wheelbase is 82 inches, front tread 54 inches, and rear tread 65 inches.

A large electric motor—made by the Electric Vehicle Company, of Hartford, Connecticut—is mounted in front of each end of the rear axle. Each motor is geared directly to a large spur gear bolted to the spokes of its respective wheel. The gear ratio from wheel to motor is approximately 10 to 1.

The front springs consist of a transverse semielliptic pair, with one spring mounted over the other so that the arch of the inverted upper one is clamped to the arch of the lower one. At the rear, a transverse semielliptic spring is attached to two ¾-elliptic springs mounted in a fore-and-aft direction over the wheels.

The enclosed wooden body, creating an impression of great bulk, accommodated four persons on two facing seats. Luxury equipment includes a voice tube that allowed communication between passengers and the outside driver, glass windows that

The Museum's Riker electric automobile, built about 1900.

can be raised and lowered, leather-covered fenders to shield the four wheels, and electric side-lamps.

The storage batteries are housed in two large compartments that form extensions to the body—one at the front and one at the rear. The front compartment contains a single set of 12 cells, and the rear one holds three sets, making 48 cells altogether. Since the wiring from cell to cell no longer is in place, the exact system used cannot be determined.

The exposed seat for the driver and the footman is seven feet above ground, over the rear battery compartment. The steering tiller, at the left of the seat, is attached to the upper end of a long, vertically mounted shaft that is connected to the left steering knuckle by a long rod. In front of the driver seat is a combination 150-volt voltmeter and ammeter that indicated the state of charge and the rate of charge and discharge of the batteries. On the left is a lever that operated a horizontal, drum-type controller (located under the driver seat) that governed the speed and provided the reverse.

Contracting brake bands on the rear-wheel brake drums were operated by means of a pedal that is pivoted in the floorboard.

A motor-generator set—used in the car's garage for overnight charging of the batteries—was received with the vehicle, and it appears to be contemporary. Both the motor and generator were made by the Wagner Electric Manufacturing Company, of St. Louis, Missouri. The motor is a 5-horsepower, 208-volt, single-phase, alternating-current, 60-cycle unit; and the generator is a 125-volt, direct-current unit capable of charging at a rate of 28 ampere hours at 1,800 revolutions per minute. A Weston voltmeter, Weston ammeter, circuit breakers, fuses, switches, a rheostat, and a variable resistance complete the charging equipment.

Autocar

1901
Gift of Autocar Company in 1922

This 4-passenger car, one of the first shaft-driven automobiles made in the United States, was designed by Louis S. Clarke, vice president and consulting engineer of the Autocar Company. In November 1901 it was driven from the factory in Ardmore, Pennsylvania, over frozen, rutty, country roads to the automobile show at the old Madison Square Garden in New York City in six hours and five minutes—a commendable performance.

The body, with a rear entrance to the tonneau, is constructed principally of mahogany, and the frame, which carries four full-elliptic springs, is of wood reinforced with steel. The wheelbase is 66½ inches, the tread 56 inches.

The upper of two handles standing to the left of the driver seat is the steering control; the lower handle is the gearshift.

Detailed view of the unhooded front shows how the water tank of the 1901 Autocar is mounted on the front of the dash.

The driver operated the clutch by means of a lever located between the body molding and the seat cushion; he controlled the carburetor throttle by twisting the handle of the same lever. A small handle for adjusting the spark is at the driver's left, outside the car's body.

There are three pedals. A ratchet-locked one, operated by the driver's left foot, actuated contracting brake bands on the drums of the rear wheels; the second, a spring-returned pedal, operated similar bands on a drum behind the transmission; the third, also spring returned, actuated a shift to place the transmission in reverse.

The axles are tubular. The front axle has a conventional tie rod, but the rear end of the drag link on the left is cut in the form of a toothed rack which meshes with a pinion on the lower end of the steering column. The rear axle has an enclosed differential and is stiffened by a brace. Torque rods lead from the top and bottom of the differential housing to a cross member at the left-center of the chassis. The wooden wheels have 14 spokes and mount 28-by-3-inch clincher tires.

The 2-cylinder, horizontal-opposed engine has a 3¾-inch bore and a 4-inch stroke. It is held in the frame by two metal strap hangers from each cylinder and is trussed by two rods from each side of the frame. The exhaust valve of each cylinder is operated by a camshaft in the crankcase between the two cylinders. The intake valves are automatic in operation,

Two views of the 1901 Autocar.

and a spark plug is located adjacent to each. The ignition timer is at the rear of the plate on the top of the crankcase. A small breather pipe also is attached to the plate. The floating-disk clutch is in the flywheel at the back of the engine.

Each cylinder has its own exhaust pipe, one going to the right of the car, the other to the left, and each leads into a separate muffler under the floor of the tonneau. There is an equalizer tube between the two exhaust pipes just in front of the two mufflers.

The carburetor (located under the front floorboard to the right) receives hot air through an intake tube. The air is heated in a circular device attached to the front of the water tank, which is secured to the front of the dash under the hood. The intake manifold from the carburetor leads to a point between the flywheel and the rear of the engine and then branches off to the intake valve chamber of each cylinder.

The cylinders are cooled with water circulated by a pump driven by a flat belt on a pulley at the front end of the crankshaft. The pump is at the lower right of the engine; the radiator is in front. The present radiator (not of the original design) has 15 horizontal pipes arranged in five tiers of three each, with cooling fins spaced along each pipe. The circuit of the water is from tank to pump, to the bottom of the jackets of the cylinders, out the top of the jackets, to the left top of the radiator, through the radiator, out the right top of the radiator, and back to the tank.

The selective-type transmission, with two speeds forward and one reverse, is housed in a separate case behind the flywheel. It is connected to the clutch in the flywheel by a short shaft, and to the differential by a drive shaft having a universal joint at each end.

The gasoline tank and the battery box are housed beneath a hinged wooden cover under the front-seat cushion.

On the rear of the dash are a Splitdorf 2-unit coil box and a 1-quart lubricator. Four oil pipes lead from sight-glasses at the bottom of the lubricator, which is a horizontal, cylindrical tank with glass ends. One pipe leads to the crankcase and one to the differential pinion bearing; the other two pipes no longer are connected. There is a flow control at the top of each pipe.

In 1954 four new tires and inner tubes, contributed by Harvey S. Firestone, Jr., were installed on the car. In 1956 the vehicle was put in running condition by the White Motor Company, Arlington, Virginia, branch, and it was repainted and reupholstered in black leather through the courtesy of the Autocar Division of White Motor Company, Exton, Pennsylvania.

Pierce

1901
Gift of Agnes C. Lyons in 1965

The George N. Pierce Company, of Buffalo, New York, began building its Motorettes in 1901, having previously manufactured bicycles. The 1901 model continued in manufacture with only minor modifications—for example, a steering wheel replaced the tiller in 1904—until 1906 when it was discontinued in favor of Pierce's heavier models. In 1903 the car sold for $950.

In September 1901 two Pierce Motorettes were entered in the 465-mile New York-to-Buffalo endurance run, and one of

The 1901 Pierce, which the manufacturer called its Motorette.

these cars completed the trial with an actual running time that averaged a little over 12 miles an hour. The manufacturer claimed that the 1901 Motorette's gasoline mileage was between 30 and 35 miles per gallon and that its low-gear speed was five miles an hour and its high-gear speed 25 miles an hour. The manufacturer admitted, however, that 15 miles an hour was the highest speed that could be maintained for even a moderate distance.

A 3½-horsepower De Dion Bouton single-cylinder, water-cooled engine bearing the number 3008 lies just forward of the rear axle. A horizontal, finned-tube radiator is located under the front part of the body. The water circulated from the radiator to the engine, then to a tank on the body above the engine, and then back to the radiator. A float-equipped carburetor received gasoline from a tank under the seat and warm air from a duct running through the center of the water tank. Also under the seat is a small oil tank equipped with a hand pump which forced oil to the engine. A chain connects the engine to a starting crank in front of the right rear wheel.

These automobiles were sold with only two speeds as standard equipment, but the Museum's car also has a reverse gear that was optional equipment costing $50. In high gear only, the pinion on the crankshaft and the spur gear on the driving axle are in action, the power being transmitted through spur pinion compensating gear. Low-speed gear is of the planetary type.

Controls consist of four small levers, located on the steering column, and two pedals. The largest of the levers places the transmission in high gear when it is put in the left position and in low gear when it is moved to the right; the small lever to the left is the spark control; and the other two levers, on the right, are carburetor controls. The right pedal operates the external contracting brakes on the small rear-wheel drums; the other pedal operates the reversing mechanism. The ignition switch is on the front of the seat framing.

The body rests on four elliptic springs. The frame is tubular. Behind the dash is a package or tool compartment. Two Never-out oil lamps are mounted on the dash and a double acting warning bell is suspended from the floor boards. The wire wheels carry 26-by-3-inch double-tube tires.

White Steam Automobile

1902

Gift of White Company in 1928

This steam car was made by the White Sewing Machine Company in Cleveland, Ohio. Its maker's plate bears patent dates from September 22, 1896, to October 29, 1901, and it shows that the car was number 260.

The 2-cylinder engine (mounted beneath the seat) is of the double-acting type with link reversing gear. Ball bearings are used in the main journals and eccentrics. The slides and crossheads, hardened and ground, were lubricated from automatic oil cups. The cylinders were lubricated from a specially designed cup which held enough oil for about 10 hours of operation. The exhaust steam was so muffled that it was practically noiseless. There is no condenser on the Museum's car, but this feature is found on later White steamers.

The semiflash boiler (also mounted beneath the seat) consists of spiral coils of seamless tubing placed one above another and surrounded by a casing of insulating material. The successive horizontal coils of tubing are connected by pipes that pass up and over the top coil so that the water entering at the top could not go through the coils by gravity but was held in place by pump action. The upper coils acted as heaters, and the amount of water converted into steam in the lower coils varied in accordance with the amount of steam being used by the engine. The steam was superheated in the lowest coil, and this resulted in economical operation and an almost invisible exhaust. The chimney consists of a tube that leads from the fire box to the center of another, horizontal, tube behind the seat.

No fixed water level had to be maintained, so there was no water gauge to be watched; and, since the water supply was controlled automatically by the steam pressure, no hand regulation of the fuel was required. An auxiliary hand water pump (near the driver's right leg) was used in starting and to take the place of the power pump if it became inoperative. The water was carried in a 20-gallon copper tank behind—and partially surrounding—the boiler casing.

Gasoline, used as the fuel, was carried in an 8-gallon cylindrical tank under the footboard. It was forced through the

vaporizing coil to the main burner by pressure from a hand-operated air pump (near the driver's left leg) that could be operated from the seat. A 40-pound air-pressure gauge on the dash indicated the pressure in the fuel tank.

The burner was lighted by running a small amount of gasoline into a drip cup and then lighting it with a match to heat a pilot light. The flame of the pilot light heated the vaporizing coil and lighted the main burner. The pilot light was kept burning while the car was in use.

The driver operated the throttle by means of a handle on a vertical shaft on the side of the body at his right. To open the throttle, he pulled the handle back.

The highly arched axles of heavy seamless tubing are connected at each side of the car by a fore-and-aft reach-rod of hickory. The rear axle is divided, with an enclosed differential connecting its halves. A chain connects the differential's driving sprocket with the engine's crankshaft sprocket.

The wire-spoke wheels have 30-by-3½-inch clincher tires. The front wheels turn on swiveled steering knuckles connected by a tie rod. The left knuckle is connected to the steering shaft, which is pivoted on the body and turned by means of a tiller.

The driver used a pedal at his right foot to contract a brake band on the differential; and he used a small lever near his right leg to alter the position of the reversing links of the valve mechanism.

The body, with a single seat that accommodates two persons, is supported on the running gear by four full-elliptic springs, one at each corner of the frame. A tool compartment with a hinged door is built into the rear of the body, and the top of this compartment provides a deck on which there is a large wicker basket. A buggy-type top, two kerosene headlamps, and a kerosene tail-lamp complete the equipment.

This steam automobile was restored in 1964 by Dale C. Price of Cambridge, Maryland.

The White steam automobile of 1902.

Franklin

1902
Purchased from H. H. Franklin Manufacturing Company in 1937

According to the late H. H. Franklin, the Museum's 1902 Franklin was the first of his cars to be sold and the third to be built, two earlier one having been retained by the factory for experimental uses. The original owner, S. G. Averell of Ogdensburg, New York, purchased the car in 1902, paying $1,250, but Franklin bought it back from him in June 1916. The Smithsonian purchased it from the H. H. Franklin Manufacturing Company in 1937 when that pioneer auto firm was liquidated.

The Franklin's angle-iron frame has a 71-inch wheelbase and carries a wooden body having two leather-upholstered seats. Its wire-spoke wheels, with their original rims overmounted

S. G. Averell in his 1902 car, the first Franklin auto sold by the H. H. Franklin Manufacturing Company.

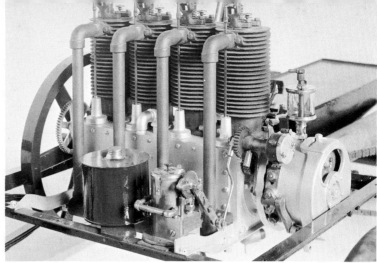

The 1902 Franklin's 7-horsepower engine and a view of its carburetor and throttle valve.

with newer ones, now have 30-by-3-inch clincher tires instead of the original 28-by-3-inch ones. The air-cooled engine is mounted transversely at the front of the frame. The front axle and the rear-axle housing, both tubular, support four full-elliptic springs. A long chain connects the exposed differential (at left of center on the rear-axle housing) to a planetary transmission at the left end of the engine. On the differential unit is a brake drum with a contracting band actuated by a right-foot pedal. Two large grease cups supplied lubrication to the two rear-wheel bearings in the ends of the rear-axle housing.

The steering wheel is on the right, and a drag link crosses from the steering-gear box to the left steering knuckle. On the steering column just below the wheel are two levers—the one on the right controls the spark and the one on the left controls the throttle, which is located about a foot above the carburetor in the vertical riser of the intake manifold. A handle for controlling the fuel mixture for the constant-level, float carburetor extends through the floorboard, and to the left of this handle is a spring-returned pedal for reversing the transmission. The forward gears are controlled by means of a lever on the right side of the body. The lever is put in central position for neutral, in rear position for low speed, and in forward position for high speed. A long narrow gasoline tank extends from a point beneath the right side of the floorboard to the rear of the car. In the center, to the left of the tank, is a muffler that runs from front to rear.

The 7-horsepower engine, with four separately cast cylinders, has a 3¼-inch bore and stroke. Integral horizontal cooling fins, about one-sixteenth inch thick, are spaced three-eighths inch apart. The crankcase, of ferrous material, has a large, rectangular access cover at the front. The flywheel and detachable hand crank are on the right end of the crankshaft.

The chassis of the Museum's 1902 Franklin.

The intake manifold, mounted transversely on the rear side of the engine, has the throttle valve at the center of a vertical riser. Each cylinder has an automatic, overhead intake valve and a pushrod-operated, overhead exhaust valve. Each of the four pushrods passes through the horizontal portion of its exhaust pipe. The four exhaust pipes, in front of the cylinders, drop to a manifold connected to a pipe that leads back to the muffler.

The camshaft was driven by external spur gears adjacent to the flywheel. The original ignition equipment has been replaced with a low-tension distributor driven by the left end of the camshaft through external gears. An eccentrically mounted arm on the timer gear operated a ratchet-controlled, mechanical oiler (in front of the engine) that pumped oil into the crankcase and, when adjusted properly, kept it at the proper level. The mechanical oiler was kept filled by a reserve tank to which it was connected.

When this automobile was restored in 1965 by Dale C. Price of Cambridge, Maryland, the left front tire was replaced but the other three tires—of the wrapped-tread type, about 1916— were retained. New inner tubes previously had been donated by Harvey S. Firestone, Jr.

The Museum's 1902 Franklin.

Indian Motorcycle

1902

Gift of Indian Motocycle Company in 1930

This motorcycle was designed in 1901 by the noted bicycle racer Oscar Hedstrom for the Springfield, Massachusetts, firm of Hendee Manufacturing Company, later known as the Indian Motocycle Company. It was built in 1902, the year that the model was first offered for sale.

The 1¾-horsepower, 1-cylinder, 4-cycle, air-cooled engine, bearing the number 150, has an automatic intake valve and a cam-actuated exhaust valve. The ignition system consists of dry cells and a coil, timer, and spark plug.

The driver advanced and retarded the timer by means of a small lever at the front of the frame on the steering head. The same lever also was used to release compression—when it was moved to the retard position it lifted the exhaust valve from its seat—and it served as the ignition switch. Fuel adjustment was controlled by means of a lever attached to the cross bar of the frame.

A two-sectioned tank on the rear fender supplied gasoline to a float-equipped Hedstrom carburetor and oil to the crankcase. The oil flowed by gravity through a sight glass. A small exhaust pipe leads to a muffler beneath the crankcase.

A double-reduction sprocket-and-chain drive (on the left side of the frame) transmitted power from the engine to the rear wheel. Since the machine had no clutch or change gear, the engine was connected to the wheel at all times. Supplementary power was available from a pedal-and-chain drive (on the right side) that incorporates a New Departure coaster brake that engaged when the driver applied a slight backward pressure on the pedals. The pedals remained at rest when the engine was propelling the machine.

The diamond-type frame is of tubular construction; the wooden-rimmed wheels carry 28-by-1½-inch, single-tube, pneumatic tires; and the complete machine weighs just under 100 pounds.

The 1902 Indian motorcycle.

Winton Racing Car

1902

Gift of Winton Engine Company in 1929

Alexander Winton drives his Winton racing car "Bullet No. 1" on a dirt track in Cleveland in 1902. He broke several records that year on another track in Cleveland.

This 4-cylinder Winton, built in 1902 and known as the "Bullet No. 1," was Alexander Winton's second racing car. He had built a 1-cylinder car for the first Gordon Bennett road race, held in France in 1900.

On September 16, 1902, Winton drove this car—on a Cleveland, Ohio, horse-race track—10 miles in 10 minutes and 50 seconds, an average speed of 55.38 miles an hour that was remarkable at that time. The next year, on March 28 at Daytona Beach, he drove the same car a mile in 52.2 seconds, an average speed of 68.96 miles an hour.

The massive, water-cooled, 4-cylinder engine has a bore of 6 inches and a stroke of 7 inches, with a total piston displacement of 792 cubic inches. It is mounted at the front of the chassis, with the crankshaft parallel to the sides of the frame. On each side of the crankcase are two arms which support the

Alexander Winton at the wheel of his 1902 racing car at Daytona Beach in March 1903.

The carburetor and part of the intake manifold of the Winton "Bullet No. 1," and (below) a view of the disassembled carburetor.

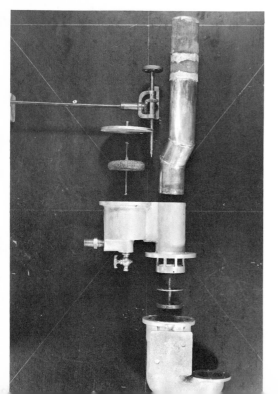

engine in the frame. The crankcase and the base are of aluminum, and the 1-piece water jacket of the four cast-iron cylinders is made of brass sheeting, screwed in place. The use of these materials was an important factor in keeping down the weight of the car. Other engine parts made of aluminum are the timing-gear cover (at the front), intake manifold, covers for the cages of the overhead intake valves, water pump, carburetor, and base of the air pump.

The engine is of the 4-cycle type, with camshaft-actuated exhaust valves on the left side and automatic, overhead intake valves directly above them. The carburetor, on the right side of the engine, is connected to the intake manifold on the left side by a metal tube that leads up the right side and over the top of the engine. The exhaust ports lead to a heavy sheet-metal exhaust manifold that connects to a large muffler under the car on the left side. A cut-out fitted to the rear of the muffler was controlled by a lever in front of the driver seat. The muffler usually was removed before the car was to be raced.

A crank-throw on the forward projection of the crankshaft drove a reciprocating-piston air pump that supplied compressed air for a unique speed-control system. When the engine was running, compressed air was supplied to the lower ends of small cylinders that enclose pistons on the stems of the four intake valves. The air pressure opposed the motion of the valves as they were being drawn open by engine suction. Two relief valves—one a foot plunger, the other a hand valve—varied the pressure on the valve pistons and thus controlled the speed of the engine. As the air pressure was reduced, the valve opening and the engine speed increased. The float-equipped carburetor does not have a throttle valve.

The oil reservoir, made of sheet brass and secured to the right side of the engine, delivered oil by gravity to a 16-unit oiler at the front of the engine above the air pump. There is a shut-off valve between the reservoir and the oiler, and each unit of the oiler is equipped with a sight glass and a metering adjustment. The oil dripped to the camshaft and engine bearings, timing gears, cylinder walls, and bearing surfaces of the air pump.

To the left of the air pump is a large, hard-rubber, low-tension ignition timer (driven from within the timing-gear cover) that was advanced and retarded by means of a lever near the steering column. There is a threaded spark-plug hole in the top of each cylinder, above the center of each piston.

The water tank, made of sheet copper with soldered seams and secured to the right side of the engine behind the oil reservoir, has an overflow pipe and a filler opening for the entire water system. The radiator, placed low at the front of the car,

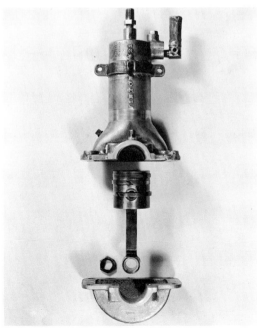

This pump on the engine of the Winton 1902 racing car supplied compressed air that controlled the opening of the intake valves. An exploded view of the pump is shown below.

consists of 54 horizontal tubes arranged in nine rows that are six tubes deep. Each tube carries dozens of cooling disks pressed into place. Adjacent ends of the tubes are connected by cast-aluminum header plates (on each side of the radiator) that have diversion channels for the control of the flow of water from side to side. A centrifugal water pump, which, like the ignition timer, is driven from within the timing-gear cover, is attached to the left side of the crankcase; its discharge opening leads into the left section of the engine's water jacket. The cooling water passed from the top of the right section of the jacket to the water tank, then into the radiator at its upper right and out at its lower left, and back to the pump.

A shaft for a starting crank extends over the right side of the radiator, and a gear is fitted to the rear end of this shaft in proximity to a similar gear secured to the extension of the crankshaft directly behind the air pump. A large idler gear is mounted loosely on a short shaft, and when it was moved rearward it engaged the two gears on the crankshaft, allowing the engine to be cranked. The linkage controlling the motion of the idler is no longer on the car. The 18-inch starting crank has a left-hand ratchet at its shaft end, and this form of ratchet and the arrangement of the rear-axle gears indicate that the engine ran counterclockwise (as viewed from the front) rather than clockwise, the usual manner.

The frame, which rests on four semielliptic springs, consists of two wooden rails (2 inches thick and 3½ inches high) that are rigidly positioned by the four arms of the engine and the four arms of the transmission. There is a single wooden cross member at the rear. The differential housing is partly supported by a divided truss rod, and the two springs over the axle housing have full shackles at their ends. Radius rods at each side connect the housing to the sides of the frame, and two torque arms to the right of the gear housing connect with the transmission's right-rear support arm. The car has a 98-inch wheelbase and a 56-inch tread.

The transmission, with housing, integral supporting arms, and cover plate of aluminum, is in the center of the frame behind the engine's heavy 20-inch flywheel. It provided two forward speeds and a reverse, with the changes effected by a single sliding gear on the keyed mainshaft within the housing. When in the rear position the sliding gear engaged an idler gear, which reversed the drive; when in the center position, low speed; and when in the forward position, direct drive, without involving gearing. All the gears ran in a lubricant.

The driver shifted gear by squeezing a locking handle on the end of the inner of two vertical levers (at the right of his seat). This action lifted a control arm from one of four notches—

Oil tank and sight-drip feed system on the engine of the Winton "Bullet No. 1," and an exploded view of the low-tension ignition timer.

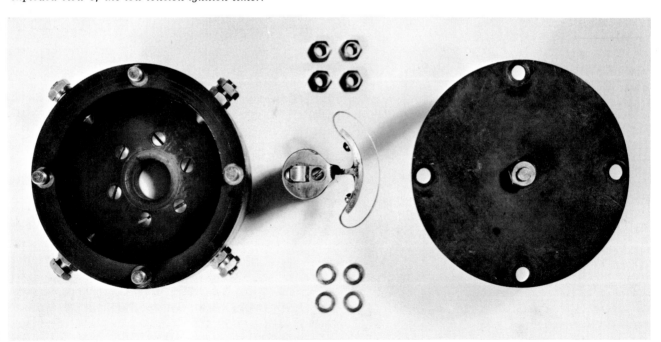

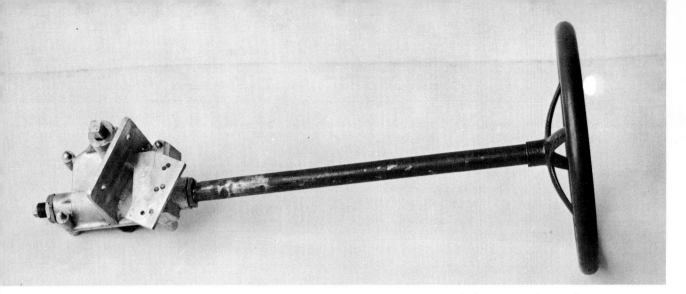

Steering column and gear box of the "Bullet No. 1." The steering-gear box is shown disassembled in photo at lower right.

representing reverse, neutral, low, and direct drive.

The clutch, a leather-faced cone within the flywheel, became disengaged by forward motion when the driver depressed the brake pedal or pushed the brake lever. It was held engaged by a very heavy coil spring. The brake pedal operated expanding shoes within bronze drums attached to the rear wheels. The hand brake, held in place by a ratchet and pawl, is connected to contracting bands on the same drums.

The rear-axle gearing is enclosed by a bronze housing, and the axle shafts are within steel housings. The bevel gears and the differential ran in a lubricant. There are 35 teeth in the driving gear and 37 in the driven gear—almost a 1-to-1 ratio. The transmission is connected to the rear-axle gearing by a short telescoping drive shaft having a universal joint at front and rear. The two pieces of this shaft are keyed so that the rear piece, with the smaller diameter, could slide backward or forward within the hollow one in front.

The front axle—a solid steel forging with a kick-up at each end—is held in place by the two springs, which have full shackles at their rear ends. Spindles on the ends of the axle are

connected by a tie rod. A long drag link connects the pitman arm of a double-threaded worm and sector (within the aluminum steering-gear housing) to the axle's right spindle. The hub and four spokes of the steering wheel are of bronze, as are the spring hangers for the six full shackles of the four springs.

The low wooden body, which is fitted to the frame, has a single seat, on the right side. A gasoline tank of sheet copper is beneath the seat, which had to be removed to gain access to the tank's filler cap. The distributor and air pump are covered by a hinged, rectangular sheet of aluminum.

In 1962, when the car was completely restored by the National Auto Top Company, Washington, D. C., a replica was made of the original engine-hood, and clincher tires, 32 inches in diameter, were mounted on the wooden-spoke wheels. The hood and tires were missing when the Smithsonian received the car in 1929.

The Winton "Bullet No. 1" was one of the foremost racing cars of its day, and it is one of the oldest in existence. It was not a converted passenger vehicle, as was often the case with racing cars at that time; rather, it was a machine that was carefully and specifically designed for racing. None of the car's parts appears to have been added as an afterthought; however, its ornate wooden scrolls and paintwork—apparently considered necessary by body builders—are incongruous notes in an otherwise strictly functional design.

Alexander Winton in his "Bullet No. 1."

Winton Racing Car

1903

Gift of Winton Engine Company in 1929

Alexander Winton's third racing car, called "Bullet No. 2," was one of the first automobiles to use an 8-cylinder, in-line engine. It was built for the fourth Gordon Bennett road race, held in Ireland in 1903, and Winton drove it in that race until a minor mechanical failure forced him to withdraw. Other drivers, including Earl Kiser and Barney Oldfield, later raced the car in various contests in the United States. At Daytona Beach on January 28, 1904, with Oldfield at the wheel, the "Bullet No. 2" covered a mile in 43 seconds. This speed, equivalent to 83.7 miles an hour, was very close to the world's record at that time.

The car's straight-eight engine consists of two 4-cylinder, in-line motors bolted together, with the cylinders lying in a horizontal plane. The 5¼-inch bore and 6-inch stroke produced a total piston displacement of 1,029 cubic inches. The engine is mounted in the center of the chassis, with the crankshaft parallel to the sides of the frame. The two aluminum crankcases are attached to the frame's left member by four integrally cast arms; the two 4-cylinder blocks are secured to the right member.

The two crankshafts are bolted together in the space between the two crankcases, as are the two camshafts. The shaft that drove the ignition distributor (now incomplete) leads up between the two engine units. This shaft was driven by the camshaft unit.

The engine is of the 4-cycle type, with cam-actuated exhaust valves lying horizontally at the bottom right. To the right of the exhaust valves are automatic intake valves, which would be called overhead valves had the engine been mounted upright. Each 4-cylinder block is fitted with an aluminum intake manifold that had its own carburetor, but both carburetors are missing. A long muffler that is suspended beneath the blocks is a replacement. The engine ran in a clockwise direction (when viewed from the front).

Access plates above each of the eight throws of the crankshaft enabled ready inspection of the bearings. Each 4-cylinder unit has five main bearings. A sheet-brass oil reservoir, with a

Alexander Winton at the wheel of his "Bullet
No. 2." In the photo below, taken at Kilcullen,
Ireland, in 1903, John J. Jack occupies the
passenger seat.

shut-off valve, is secured above the front cylinders. It delivered oil by gravity to a float-equipped, constant-level oiler on each set of cylinders. From the two oilers, the oil flowed to the ten main bearings, the eight cylinder walls, the timing gears, and the air pump.

When the engine was running, the air pump (secured to the outside of the crankcase of the front unit and operated by a rod connected to the skirt of the third piston) supplied compressed air to the small pistons on the ends of the eight intake valves. Two relief valves—one a foot plunger and the other a hand valve—served to vary the pressure as desired. The lower the pressure, the farther the intake valves would be drawn open and the faster the engine would run.

The two centrifugal water pumps—one beneath each engine unit—are made of aluminum and are connected by a shaft, with the front pump driven by a shaft that extends back from the aluminum cover over the timing gears at the front of the engine. The water jackets of the two blocks also are made of aluminum, and the water manifolds are aluminum castings. The water tank, integral with the top water jacket of the front cylinder, is of sheet brass and contains a filler cap and an overflow pipe for the entire water system.

The radiator, placed low at the front of the car, consists of 42 horizontal tubes arranged across the front in seven rows that are six tubes deep. Each tube carries dozens of cooling disks, and the adjacent ends of the tubes are connected by cast-aluminum header plates on each side of the radiator. The cooling water passed from the top water jackets of the cylinders into the water tank and then through the radiator (entering at the upper right and leaving at the lower left) and back to the pumps, which sent the water into the bottom water jackets of the cylinders.

The driver advanced and retarded the low-tension ignition timer by means of a small lever at his seat, but the connection that linked the lever and the timer is missing. It is not known where the battery was located. At one time eight coils were secured to the inside of the body above the rear crankcase, but when the car came to the Museum only four incomplete coils were still in place. There was evidence, however, that originally the coils were located in a box under the seat, and such a box was constructed when the Museum restored the car in the 1960s. There is a threaded spark-plug hole in the center of each cylinder head.

The frame consists of two wooden rails (2 inches thick and 3½ inches high), which are rigidly secured by the two engine units, and of two wooden cross members, one at the front and one at the rear. The car has a wheelbase of 111 inches, a tread of 56 inches, and wooden-spoke wheels that originally carried

34-by-4½-inch clincher tires. Since the tires that were on the car were badly deteriorated, they were replaced with new tires of suitable dimensions.

The rear-axle gearing is enclosed by a bronze housing, and the axle shafts are within tubular steel housings. The axle housing is attached to the frame by semielliptic springs with full shackles at their ends, to the sides of the frame by radius rods at each side, and to the rear cross member by two parallel torque arms. Helping to support the differential is a divided truss rod beneath its housing. Leather rebound straps, with their ends attached to the frame, pass beneath the axle hous-

The Winton 1903 racing car as it appears today.

ings on each side of the differential. The bevel gears and the differential ran in lubricant. Three grease cups, fitted to the differential housing, provided lubrication for the pinion bearing and differential bearings. The gear ratio is approximately 1¼-to-1.

The front axle—a solid steel forging with a kick-up at each end—is held in place by two semielliptic springs with full shackles at their rear ends. A tie rod connects the spindles on the ends of the axle; and a 4-foot drag link connects the right spindle to the pitman arm of a worm and gear sector in the steering gear's aluminum housing. The steering wheel's hub and six spokes are of aluminum.

Since forward speed was by direct drive only, there is no change-gear box. A short drive shaft, with two universal joints, connects a large, metal, gear-toothed disk to the rear-axle housing. The disk, located directly behind the flywheel at the rear of the engine, has the same diameter as the flywheel and can be connected to it by means of a clutch of the internal-expanding-shoe type.

Reverse is effected by means of a 6-foot auxiliary shaft (lying parallel with the engine at its upper left) that extends from the front end of the crankshaft to the disk behind the flywheel. Keyed on the rear end of this auxiliary shaft is a small sliding gear that can mesh with the teeth of the disk. Another small gear (fitted to the front end of the crankshaft) can mesh with an idler gear which, in turn, can mesh with still another gear (on the front end of the auxiliary shaft) that has a clutch built into its hub.

When he wanted to reverse, the driver had to push forward, for a slight distance, a long lever (outside the body, on his right) to disengage the main clutch in the flywheel; push a short lever (inside the body, on the left) to engage the sliding gear on the auxiliary shaft; and, finally, push a long lever (at his left) to engage the clutch on the front of the auxiliary shaft. Power then was transmitted, via the auxiliary shaft, from the front of the engine to the drive shaft, which would turn in a counterclockwise direction (as viewed from the front).

A shaft for a starting crank extends from the crankshaft through a space provided between the radiator tubes at the front of the car.

Brake drums (probably of cast iron) on the rear wheels have external bands and internal shoes. The bands contracted when the driver pushed the long clutch lever to its forward limit; they released, and the clutch in the flywheel became engaged, when he pulled the lever back. The shoes expanded when the driver depressed a brake pedal with his left foot.

When it was received at the Smithsonian in 1929 the car had a single bucket seat, on the right; the side panels of the low wooden body were covered with sheet aluminum; and there was a single lever on the right side. Contemporary photographs (some of which are reproduced here) indicated, however, that the car had undergone numerous changes from time to time in its racing career, apparently to improve its performance. For example, the pictures showed that there had been two bucket seats, and two levers on the right side. When the Museum's shop restored the car in the 1960s, the aluminum panels were removed, revealing the damaged wooden sides with their original lettering; a new wooden body was con-

Alexander Winton with Barney Oldfield in the
"Bullet No. 2."

structed, according to the original design; two bucket seats were installed; and the cylindrical gasoline tank behind the seat was replaced with a larger one, as shown in the earliest photographs. Between the steering column and the front of the car are three hinged covers of sheet aluminum that permitted access to the various parts of the machinery.

Winton

1903

Gift of H. Nelson Jackson in 1944

This Winton was the first automobile to cross the continent from coast to coast. H. Nelson Jackson bought the car second-hand at San Francisco in 1903, and on May 23 he and Sewall K. Crocker left that city on their transcontinental trip. They reached New York City on July 26, after traveling over roads and trails that would be impassable for today's low-slung cars. Although the trip took 64 days, only 44 of these were used in actual travel.

The water-cooled engine, of the 2-cylinder, 4-cycle, horizontal-opposed type, is suspended from two cross members of the chassis, near the center of the frame and beneath the left seat. The bore is 5¼ inches, the stroke 6 inches. The flywheel, near the center of the car, is 24 inches in diameter and its rim is 2½ inches thick and 3½ inches wide; it rotated in a vertical plane parallel with the sides of the frame.

This car is one of the earliest standard-production automobiles to be equipped with multiple carburetion—each of its cylinders is fitted with a carburetor. An exhaust pipe leads from each cylinder to a common muffler having a cut-out that the driver operated by means of a small lever in front of his seat. An enclosed train of gears, on the left side of the engine, drove the two exhaust camshafts, water pump, and ignition timer. The timing-gear cover is of aluminum.

The water system includes a storage tank, water jackets on the two cylinders, a centrifugal pump of aluminum, a radiator, and the necessary piping. The radiator—behind an opening in the wooden hood at the front—consists of horizontal tubing fitted with radiating disks. Behind it is a cylindrical tank having two separate sections, one for water and one for gasoline. The filler cap is at the top of the water tank, and there is an overflow pipe within the tank. A pipe leads from the water jackets at the top of the engine cylinders to the bottom of the radiator. The top of the radiator is connected to the side of the water tank, and a pipe connects the bottom of the tank to the pump, the casing of which is cast integrally with the water manifold at the bottom of the two cylinders.

A pipe leading from the bottom of the gasoline section of

the tank carried fuel to both carburetors. On top of the tank, next to the gasoline filler cap, is a handwheel for operating the shut-off valve. A hinged aluminum cover on the wooden hood provided access to both sections of the tank.

The carburetors are of rather massive construction and have aluminum parts; and their float bowls are equipped with cork floats. Each carburetor incorporates an automatic, suction-type intake valve for its cylinder. The extent to which the valves opened was controlled by an air-pressure system similar to the one on the Winton racing cars of 1902 and 1903. When the engine was running, an air pump—located near the rear cylinder of the engine and operated by means of a rod connected to the skirt of the front cylinder's piston—sent compressed air to the two intake valves. A foot-operated plunger and a hand valve are connected to the piping, and the extent to which either one was opened caused a corresponding drop in pressure. The lower the pressure, the more the intake valves would open and the faster the engine would run. The carburetors have no throttle valves.

Each cylinder of the engine has a petcock for the release of compression. The petcocks were operated by means of long rods reaching to the right side of the body beneath the seat and floorboard, where the person cranking the car could control them easily. When the petcocks were closed, clips held the rods in the proper position and prevented accidental opening.

The ignition system consists of a spark plug in each cylinder, low-tension timer, Jefferson spark coil, battery, and switch. The driver advanced and retarded the timer by means of a small lever to the right of the muffler cut-out lever at the front of his seat.

The transmission, at the right of the engine and with its mainshaft in line with and connected to the engine crankshaft, was of a very advanced design for its time, but it was a logical development of the transmission designed for the 1898 Winton, described earlier. Its cubical, aluminum housing, with a removable cover of the same material, contains two parallel shafts, on each of which are three wide-faced spur gears placed so that the gears on one shaft constantly are meshed with the opposite gears on the other shaft. An idler gear, for reverse, is interposed between the two gears of the right-hand set. The first gear on the mainshaft is free to rotate on the shaft. Its hub has an extension (outside the housing) that is integral with the driving sprocket (located between the housing and the flywheel); and its mating gear is pinned to the countershaft. The other two gears are pinned to the mainshaft, while their mating gears are free to turn on the countershaft.

Each of the three gears free to turn is fitted with a clutch in its hub, and the driver could obtain low speed, direct drive

The first car to travel coast to coast across the United States—the Museum's 2-cylinder 1903 Winton.

(high), or reverse drive through use of two vertical clutch levers at his right. For low speed he pulled the left lever, causing the center gear on the countershaft to clutch; for reverse he pushed the same lever, causing the right gear on the countershaft to clutch; and for direct drive he pulled the right lever, causing the left gear of the mainshaft—and hence the driving sprocket—to clutch directly to the crankshaft extension. When he pushed the right lever, a band contracted around a brake drum attached to the driving sprocket.

A hand-crank extension of the mainshaft is on the right side of the car.

An oil tank on the dash furnished lubricant to the bushings through a set of holes in brackets within the transmission. The gears rotated in the same lubricant. A plug in the bottom of the housing could be removed to drain the oil.

The car's frame is comprised of two side members and a cross member at front and rear, all angle-iron sections. Other cross members support the engine and the steering-gear housing in the frame.

Enclosed in the aluminum steering-gear housing are a worm and sector with a short pitman arm that is connected to the spindle of the left front wheel by a transverse drag link. The front axle is a solid bar attached to the frame by two semi-elliptic springs (one at each side) that have full shackles at their rear ends only. Spindles on the axle ends are connected by a tie rod behind the axle. The steering wheel could be tilted up on the steering column, giving the driver easy access to his seat.

The tubular rear axle encloses half-axles. The sprocket of the exposed differential unit is driven by a chain from the driving sprocket on the output shaft of the transmission. The rear-axle assembly, externally strengthened by three truss rods, is attached to the frame by two semielliptic springs (one on each side) that have full shackles at their ends. Two external, adjustable radius rods, fitted to the axle assembly, prevented forward or backward motion of the springs. Contracting bands on brake drums inside the rear wheels were operated by a pedal that incorporates a multiple-toothed ratchet for locking it in the depressed position. This brake pedal, which pivots on the front engine support, was returned to the "off" position by means of a long, narrow coil spring.

The wooden-spoke wheels have nondemountable rims fitted with old (but not original) 32-by-4-inch clincher tires that contain inner tubes contributed by Harvey S. Firestone, Jr., in 1954. The car's wheelbase is 91 inches and its tread 56 inches.

The horizontal, cylindrical oil tank, made of brass and having a capacity of about one quart, is secured to the dashboard in front of the driver. Six oil lines, each incorporating a small sight glass, lead from the bottom of the tank. The oil flow in these lines could be metered or shut off by means of six adjustable valves at the top of the tank. The first and third lines (from the right) lead into the transmission; the fifth and sixth lead to the main bearings of the engine. The second and fourth lines are disconnected, but the fourth line probably led to the air pump.

The body, removable hood, and four laminated fenders are of wood; the two side step-plates are iron; and the two seats are upholstered in tufted black leather. The single headlamp and a bulb horn, originally with the car, are missing. A spare tire is attached to the left side of the body, but a spare was carried on the front of the hood when the car made its transcontinental trip. None of the five tires now with the car was used on the famous trip, but in the tonneau, which is covered with a tarpaulin, are some of the tools and spare parts that were carried from San Francisco in 1903.

The car was restored in 1962 by Dale C. Price, of Cambridge, Maryland, but the original upholstery was retained. Later, appropriate side-lamps were installed, to replace the missing originals.

Cadillac

1903

Gift of Cadillac Motor Car Company in 1923

This Model A Cadillac was built in Detroit during the Cadillac Automobile Company's first year of production in 1903. It sold for $850 when new.

The 1-cylinder, water-cooled engine (built by Leland and Faulconer) has a 5-inch bore and stroke, giving a total piston displacement of 98.2 cubic inches. It is mounted horizontally in the frame, with the cylinder toward the rear. The hand crank can be attached to the crankshaft at the flywheel, which is near the middle of the car on the left side. The engine is not the original one; it was taken from a Cadillac of about 1906, as indicated by the oiler and by the method of cranking. The present engine is cranked in a counterclockwise direction from the left side, but the original engine could be cranked from either side of the car by means of a secondary shaft connected to the crankshaft by sprockets and chain. This secondary shaft is still in place beneath the body, but it is no longer connected to the crankshaft, which has no sprocket.

Ignition was by spark plug and high-tension coil. The driver advanced and retarded the spark by means of a short lever in a slot at his right. The coil is in a compartment at the left front of the body, and the dry cells are in a box suspended from the left front corner of the floorboard. The driver controlled the engine speed by operating a lever (working on a segment beneath the steering wheel) which regulated the opening of the mechanically operated inlet valve. The exhaust valve leads into a short pipe which, in turn, leads into a sheet-metal muffler beneath the body at the right rear.

The water tank, in a compartment at the right front of the body, and the remainder of the water system were filled through a pipe beneath the left front seat. The radiator consists of a long, seamless, copper tube (five-eighths inch in outside diameter) over which are slipped hundreds of copper radiating disks spaced three-eighths inch apart. The tube is bent and shaped so that it forms a 12-tube unit that is six tubes high and two tubes deep, with all tubes horizontal. A centrifugal pump circulated the water through the jackets of the cylinder and through the water tank and the radiator.

The Museum's 1903 Cadillac after its reconditioning in 1955.

The planetary transmission, with steel pinions and bronze gears, provided two speeds forward and a reverse. The driver engaged low speed by depressing a pedal, high speed by moving forward a long lever at his right, and reverse by moving the same lever to its rear position. The gearshift lever was in neutral when it was in the center position.

A single chain transmitted power to a differential at the center of the divided rear axle. Brake drums are attached to the halves of the axle at the sides of the differential. The two contracting brake bands were actuated simultaneously by a spring-returned pedal which now is equipped with a ratchet-and-pawl device (not originally with the car) that was designed to hold the pedal locked in the depressed position so that it could be used as a parking brake.

A rack and a gear (adjustable for wear) are mounted at the

base of the steering column and are connected to the left front wheel's steering knuckle by a drag link. A tie rod connects the steering knuckles of the front wheels. The front axle is tubular.

The angle-steel frame is carried on four semielliptic springs. The position of the rear axle is maintained by adjustable stay rods (one on each side) that run from the center of the frame. The car's wheelbase is 70 inches; its tread is 53 inches; and its wooden-spoke wheels, fitted with ball bearings, carry 30-by-3½-inch clincher tires.

To the left of the gasoline tank, which is beneath the driver seat, is a mechanical oiler that was a feature of the 1906 engine now in the car. This oiler, belt-driven from a pulley on the crankshaft of the engine, has four outlets that served the engine bearings and the cylinder wall.

The car's wooden body has two seats that could accommodate four persons. A single door at the rear provided entrance to the tonneau, which could be removed completely to convert the car to a two-passenger runabout. There was no top or windshield. The four fenders are of metal, as are the three stepplates—one on each side and one at the rear; the three kerosene lamps—two at the front and one at the rear—are of brass. A bulb horn is attached to the steering column. A wicker basket is suspended from each side of the tonneau, over the fenders. Although the baskets (given by Charles P. Ashley in 1934) were added to the car after it came to the Museum, they are authentic accessories that provided storage for equipment and luggage. The vehicle weighs about 1,350 pounds.

New tires and tubes (contributed by Harvey S. Firestone, Jr.) were installed in 1954; and in the following year the car was cleaned, repainted in red, and reupholstered in tufted black leather by the Antique Auto Shop in Northfield, New Jersey, through the courtesy of the Cadillac Motor Car Division of General Motors Corporation.

Oldsmobile

1903

Bequest of Thomas A. Peabody in 1944

One of the most popular cars of its day was the low-priced, light, curved-dash Oldsmobile runabout that was continuously produced—with only minor changes in design—from 1901 to 1906. Despite its large, 1-cylinder engine, the car was known for its economy of operation and for its quiet, smooth performance. The Museum's 1903 Oldsmobile sold for $650 at the Olds Motor Works in Detroit.

The engine, with a 4½-inch bore and a 6-inch stroke, ran at a maximum speed of a little over 700 revolutions per minute. It is placed horizontally, with the cylinder head at the rear of the car and the flywheel below the seat. The inlet and exhaust valves (in a chamber at the side of the cylinder head) were operated mechanically by rockers working from cams on a shaft (parallel to and outside the cylinder) that was turned—by gearing at the crankshaft—at half crankshaft speed. Opposite the exhaust valve cam on this shaft, and in a different plane, is an auxiliary cam. To reduce the compression while the engine was being cranked, the driver depressed a foot-button that caused the exhaust rocker to shift so that its roller would bear against both the cam proper and the auxiliary cam, thus preventing the exhaust valve from seating completely. A removable cover made both valves accessible for inspection.

The high-tension ignition was fed by a set of 6-volt dry cells, with the current passing through a trembler coil to a spark plug that is screwed into the end of the cylinder. The time of firing was controlled by a commutator on the half-speed camshaft, and the gasoline charge was ignited when the piston was at approximately top dead center. The driver advanced and retarded the spark timing by means of a small lever at his right.

The constant-level, float-type carburetor (made by George M. Holley of Bradford, Pennsylvania) has a throttle valve that is connected by linkage to a pedal. The gasoline tank is beneath the right side of the rear deck and above the carburetor.

Exhaust gasses passed through a muffler below the left side of the engine.

Cooling fins and a water jacket surround the cylinder, with

the fins being at the end nearer the crankcase. The water tank is at the left rear, beneath the deck. The radiator, suspended horizontally beneath the floorboard, is a long tube (bent and shaped to form a compact unit) with hundreds of radiating disks slipped over it. Water was circulated by a gear pump driven by the left end of the crankshaft. All water connections are rubber hose.

Grease cups are fitted to the two main bearings, and a sight-feed oil cup provided lubrication to the cylinder wall. The flow from the oil cup could be adjusted by means of a lever mounted on the wooden panel at the front of the seat. There is a drain cock in the bottom of the crankcase.

The handle of the starting crank is so situated on the right side of the body that the driver could crank the engine while he was seated in the car. A sprocket on the hand crankshaft is chain-connected to a sprocket on the engine crankshaft; and an

The 1903 Oldsmobile.

overrunning clutch within the hub of the latter sprocket prevented the engine, once it started, from driving the crank handle.

The planetary transmission, suspended at the center of the frame, provided two forward speeds and a reverse. The gear for the low forward speed and the gear for the reverse were operated by band-and-drum clutches; the high-speed gear was operated by a friction compression clutch. A lever at the driver's right is a vertical extension of a single shaft carrying three eccentrics—with the three throws in different directions—that actuated the three clutches individually. It actuated the two low-speed clutches by tightening the bands around the drums, and it actuated the high-speed clutch by means of a bell crank that moved in a direction longitudinal to the main shaft. The high-speed clutch was engaged when the driver pushed the lever to full forward position.

The brake pedal is connected to a contracting band on a drum located on the transmission shaft between the low-speed and reverse drums; and a sprocket on the transmission between the reverse drum and the brake drum is connected by chain to the differential unit on the rear axle. The band of the brake drum on the differential unit is actuated by means of a lever adjacent to the gear-shift and spark levers.

The front axle and the rear-axle housing are tubular, and each is strengthened by a truss rod that runs beneath it. Pivoted steering spindles at the ends of the front axle are connected by a tie rod. Between the steering-pillar post and the arm leading to the center of the tie rod is a full-elliptic spring which turns with the tiller and prevents road shock from reaching it.

The wooden-spoke, artillery-type wheels are mounted with 28-by-3-inch clincher tires. The front wheels are on tapered roller bearings; the rear wheels are on straight roller bearings lubricated by grease cups.

The rectangular frame of channel steel is mounted on two long, truss-shaped springs (one spring on each side) that connect the front axle to the rear-axle housing; the connection at the rear is adjustable to take up slack in the driving chain. Wheelbase is 66 inches; the tread, 55 inches.

The bolts that secure the wooden body to the frame pass through rubber blocks that lessened any chassis vibration that might have reached the body. The car's four fenders and two step-plates are of metal. Its three lamps, two at the front and one at the rear, burn oil.

This Oldsmobile was in use through 1941, and the Museum received it three years later. In 1956 it was sent to Lansing, Michigan, where it was repainted black and reupholstered in tufted black leather by the Oldsmobile Division of General Motors Corporation.

Columbia Electric Automobile

1904

Gift of Mrs. Sewell M. Johnson in 1933

The Columbia Mark LX electric runabout was first introduced in the fall of 1903 by the Electric Vehicle Company of Hartford, Connecticut. The one in the Museum's collection—used by Dr. J. O. Skinner until 1931—represents a type of vehicle often used by doctors in the early days of motoring when an electric automobile was more reliable than a gasoline-powered car.

This car was designed to have as little dead weight as possible without sacrificing traveling capacity, safety, and durability. The lightweight running gear and body allowed a larger battery for increased storage capacity and a heavier motor for greater power. The car's maximum speed was about 15 miles an hour, and it was said to have a traveling range of 40 miles per charge. Its total weight is 1,200 pounds.

The frame consists of oak sills reinforced on each side by 1¾-inch angle steel. All springs are of the semielliptic type and are 36 inches long. The front springs are shackled at their rear ends; the rear ones at their front ends. The rear axle is large and tubular, and is equipped with roller bearings; the front one is a Collins axle with plain bearings. The car's wheelbase is 64 inches; its tread is 48 inches; and its artillery-type wheels, 24 inches in diameter, carry 30-by-3-inch clincher tires that were contributed, with inner tubes, by Harvey S. Firestone, Jr., in 1954.

The car is steered by means of a lever at the driver's left. A single controller handle, also on the left, governed the two speeds, forward and reverse.

Each of the boxlike compartments of the body (front and rear) originally contained half of the battery equipment. The batteries, 20 two-volt cells, had a capacity of 120 ampere hours at a 30-ampere discharge rate. No batteries are in the car now.

The motor, believed to have been made by General Electric Company, is of 6-pole construction, completely enclosed, and rated at 30 amperes at 40 volts. Instead of being located on the rear axle, the motor is in the body beneath the seat, a location that prolonged its life and the life of the tires.

The steel armature pinion, of the herringbone type, meshes

The Museum's 1904 Columbia electric automobile was in use until 1931.

with a herringbone gear of bronze carried on the countershaft. These gears are fully enclosed, and they operated noiselessly. The outer end of the countershaft carries the driving sprocket, which transmitted power to the rear axle by a chain. An adjustable rod holds the countershaft at a constant distance from the rear axle. The motor bearings and countershaft bearings were lubricated by oil-soaked waste carried in a small pocket on each bearing. The pockets have spring-closed covers.

The bevel-gear differential is enclosed and ran in oil. The hubs of the rear wheels carry drums with contracting brake bands actuated by means of a pedal equipped with a ratchet so that it could be locked in place.

The controller handle moved in two slots separated by an offset. The forward slot gave three forward speeds; the rear slot two backing speeds. For first forward speed the two sets of batteries, acting in parallel, connected in series with the motor and with a resistance carried in a frame beneath the body; in the second forward speed the two sets of batteries acted in parallel on the motor without the resistance; in third forward speed the two sets acted in series. The two backing speeds correspond to the first two forward speeds, with the field commutated. The controller, located under the driver seat, is of the drum type, and its contacts are of hard drawn copper. Seven cables enter the controller.

The body is of wood; the fenders are of leather stretched and sewn over a metal frame; and the folding top is of leatherette. Step-plates are attached to each side of the car. Kerosene lights and a Stewart speedometer (of much later date than the vehicle) complete the equipment.

This automobile was restored in 1962 by National Auto Top Company, Washington, D. C.

Model of Rolls-Royce

1907

Gift of Rolls-Royce, Limited, in 1947

The Museum's nonoperable quarter-scale model of the 1907 Rolls-Royce represents the "Silver Ghost," which, in 1907, ran out a 15,000-mile reliability road trial that was observed officially by the Royal Automobile Club. At the conclusion of the trial, in which the car ran 14,371 miles without any involuntary stops other than for tire troubles, the automobile was dismantled and its parts examined. Then, all parts in which the slightest measurable wear could be detected were replaced—at a cost that amounted to barely more than the equivalent of $10.

The original car, in the possession of the manufacturer, has a 6-cylinder engine with a 4½-inch bore and stroke that is capable of developing about 48 horsepower. The cylinders are cast in two groups of three, with the valves, all on one side, operating from a single camshaft located in the crankcase. The hollow crankshaft has a main bearing between each two adjacent cranks. Forced lubrication was provided. The crankcase is of aluminum, and the oil pan can be removed easily for inspection. The fuel mixture, supplied by an automatic carburetor, can be adjusted for richness from the dashboard. Speed is controlled by a centrifugal governor acting on a throttle valve. Both battery and magneto ignition are fitted to the engine, with each system using a separate set of spark plugs. The cylinders are cooled by water jackets that receive water forced from the radiator by a rotary pump. The radiator, with a belt-driven fan behind it, is in front of the engine.

The flywheel forms one member of a cone clutch arranged so that there is no external thrust; the other member of the clutch is connected to the gear box by a shaft having universal joints. The gear box has a gate change with four forward speeds and a reverse. Direct drive is obtained on third speed. Power is transmitted to the rear axle by a shaft, having a universal joint at each end, that drives the halves of the axle through bevel gears and a differential unit in a central housing that is trussed and tied to the frame by radius rods. The axle runs in ball bearings.

Each driving wheel is fitted with a brake drum and an expanding band that is operated by means of a lever. Also, a brake

The Museum's quarter-scale model of the 1907
Rolls-Royce "Silver Ghost."

AX.201

Detailed view of the Rolls-Royce model's engine compartment.

Interior of the Rolls Royce scale model.

pedal acts on a drum fitted on the drive shaft behind the gear box. The front axle is an I-section forging; its pivoted ends are fitted with ball-thrust bearings.

The frame—of channel-section, pressed steel of varying depth —is supported on four semielliptic springs. The rear ends of the back springs are carried by the ends of a transverse spring fitted to a central bracket at the rear of the frame. The artillery-type wheels have grooved pneumatic tires—the front ones 875 by 105 millimeters and the rear ones 880 by 120 millimeters. The wheelbase is 135 inches and the tread 56 inches.

The car's "Roi des Belges" body has two seats, for four persons, and an adjustable windshield. The gas tank is beneath the driver seat; and the batteries and an acetylene generator for the lamps are carried on the right running board, where spare tires also are attached.

The car weighs about 3,300 pounds, unloaded, and about 4,000 pounds with passengers and baggage.

Sears Model P Delivery Car

1911
Gift of Truly Nolen in 1964

During the brief period from 1907 to 1911 numerous carriage builders attempted to enter the automobile field by offering various types of motorized wagons. Running on carriage wheels similar to those found on light wagons, these automobiles were known as "high-wheelers." This Sears, Roebuck and Company Model P, which sold for $445 in 1911 and bears serial number 2785, is an example of this type of vehicle.

In its present state the Museum's vehicle would have served as a light delivery wagon, although the Model P originally had a removable rear seat so that it could serve also as a four-passenger motor surrey. The body is essentially of the spring-wagon type.

The car's 2-cylinder, opposed, air-cooled engine has a 4⅛-inch bore and a 4-inch stroke and is rated at 14 horsepower. Internal parts are lubricated by a mechanical force-feed oiler in combination with a splash system. The finned cylinder castings are cooled by twin fans. Combustion chambers on the fronts of the cylinder castings contain mechanically operated exhaust valves and automatic intake valves. These chambers are joined across the front by two pipes which serve as the intake and exhaust manifolds. The intake pipe leads to a Schebler carburetor and the exhaust pipe is equipped with a foot-operated cut-out. Two pipes lead from the exhaust manifold to dual mufflers in the rear.

The ignition system consists of six dry cells and a nonvibrating coil. A plug-type ignition switch is located on the outer side of the body next to the driver.

The transmission is of the friction-disk type. The combination disk and flywheel, 17 inches in diameter, is attached to the rear of the crankshaft. Another shaft, located behind the disk and at right angles to the crankshaft, carries a 16-inch fiber-faced wheel and a sprocket with a 1-inch chain that runs back to the countershaft. Sprockets at the outer ends of the countershaft carry 1-inch chains to the rear-wheel sprockets, which enclose expanding brakes. On each end of the countershaft is a friction-clutch differential, designed on the coaster-brake plan.

Steering is by tiller. On the vertical steering column are two small levers—one for carburetor control and one for spark control. A lever in front of the steering column slides the fiber-faced wheel on its shaft behind the friction disk, so that a variety of speed ratios can be obtained. One of the two pedals moves the fiber-faced wheel against the disk; the other, to the right of the first, operates the brakes.

The wooden-spoke wheels carry 38-by-2-inch solid rubber tires. These tires were installed as replacements of the deteriorated original ones when the vehicle was restored in the Museum in 1967. The body rests on four elliptic springs and has rubber-cushioned, iron snubber posts above the rear springs. A 6-gallon gas tank under the seat supposedly held enough gasoline for 150 miles of travel. A pair of oil side-lamps serve as headlamps. The vehicle's total weight is 1,200 pounds.

During the restoration of the vehicle, it was discovered that some parts, particularly the driving mechanism, had undergone some alterations. Sears cars in other collections were examined, but since these obviously had not been identical to the Museum car even when new, it could not be determined exactly how the latter had been constructed.

The 1911 Sears Model P could be used as a carriage or—when the rear seat was removed —as a light delivery wagon, as shown here.

Simplex

1912
Gift of Mr. and Mrs. John D. Adams in 1929

The Museum's 1912 Simplex, number 778 in the series of Simplex cars manufactured by Simplex Automobile Company, of New York City, was known as a 50-horsepower model, but it could develop considerably more than 50 horsepower. Capable of a speed of about 80 miles an hour and in use for 16 years—until 1928—this car represents one of the most powerful and popular automobiles of its day.

The water-cooled, 4-cylinder, 4-cycle engine is of the T-head type, with cylinders cast in pairs. Its bore and stroke, both 5¾ inches, provided a total piston displacement of 597 cubic inches. Each cylinder has an intake valve on the right side and an exhaust valve on the left. The valves are operated by two camshafts in the aluminum crankcase. The exhaust camshaft moved lengthwise by means of linkage controlled by a handle under the front of the radiator. The forward position of the camshaft gives full-charge compression. The rear position brings the compression-release cams into the paths of their respective rollers, holding the exhaust valves open during the first part of the compression stroke of their respective pistons, thus lowering the compression and aiding in starting the engine with the hand crank. The exhaust manifold leads to a muffler under the left side of the car.

A Bosch DR-4, 2-spark, dual magneto furnished the charge to the eight spark plugs—two in each cylinder. The magneto, fitted to the right front of the engine, was driven by a shaft projecting back from the timing-gear case. A similar shaft on the left side of the engine drove a water pump and (by means of sprockets and chain) a Bijur electrical generator, which was not originally with the car.

A small tank, mounted on the front of the dash above the engine, held a supply of oil that was replenished from a large tank behind the seat. The small tank contains a pump (driven by a vertical shaft geared to the rear of the intake camshaft) that forced the oil to the bearing surfaces inside the engine. The oil then drained into the pan of the crankcase. An oil-level glass on the small tank is visible to the driver, and a handle that projects through the dash operated a shut-off valve that controlled the external oil supply to the cylinder walls.

A Bijur electric starting motor (not original equipment) is suspended below the left rear part of the engine so that its gear can engage a ring gear that is shrunk on the flywheel. A primer, to assist starting in cold weather, is fitted to the intake manifold.

The frame, of 128-inch wheelbase, is supported on four semi-elliptic springs. The rear shackles of the rear springs have JM shock absorbers, and the front springs are equipped with telescopic, airplane-type "jounce preventers" made by Ernst Flentje, of Cambridge, Massachusetts. The rear wheels turn on a solid, "dead" axle. Truss rods at each end of the axle lead forward to the frame, and adjustments on the ends of these rods allowed the axle to be shifted to take up any slack in the chains. Expanding shoes in the rear-wheel brake drums were controlled by a lever at the driver's right.

The steering wheel turned a post within a column and, by means of a worm and gear in the steering-gear box, controlled the steering linkage connecting the front wheels.

The sliding-gear transmission, providing four forward speeds and a reverse, is combined with the differential in a single aluminum case in the center of the car. The driver selected a speed by means of a lever to the left of the brake lever. The driving

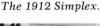

The 1912 Simplex.

sprockets of the chain drive are on the jackshafts (or output shafts) of the differential. The jackshafts also carry brake drums having contracting bands that were controlled by means of a pedal. Incorporated in the flywheel is a multiple-disk clutch controlled by a pedal to the left of the brake pedal.

Final drive is by double chain, with one chain going to each rear wheel. The front sprockets have 25 teeth and the rear sprockets 40. The Simplex was one of the last American-made cars to use chain drive, and one of the few that still had right-hand drive.

The speedster-type body, made by Holbrook of New York, is painted red with black striping. Behind the two individual bucket seats is a 13-gallon, cylindrical oil tank (12 inches in diameter and 27 inches long) equipped with a quick-opening, racing-type filler cap. Behind the oil tank is a 40-gallon, cylindrical gasoline tank 21 inches in diameter. Like the oil tank, it is 27 inches long and has a quick-opening filler cap. Gasoline was forced to the carburetor, and oil to the small tank under the hood, by pressure (of about 2 pounds per square inch) derived from the engine's exhaust, which passed to the tanks through a Lunkenheimer filter and pressure regulator. When the engine was at rest, the pressure in the tanks could be raised by means of a hand pump. A gauge at the hand pump indicated the pressure at all times, and valves on the tanks allowed the driver to shut off the pressure.

The original wooden-spoke, artillery-type wheels have been cut down to accommodate 23-inch demountable rims equipped with 33-by-5-inch, straight-side tires. Three spare rims, equipped with tires, are mounted upright behind the gasoline tank.

The car is equipped with a Mayo honeycomb radiator protected on the front by a stone-guard. The spokes of the flywheel are shaped to act as a fan behind the engine. A Juhasz carburetor (bearing the patent date of June 22, 1915) with a barrel-valve throttle has replaced the original carburetor. The driver could control the throttle by using either an accelerator pedal or a lever on a quadrant of the steering wheel. He advanced and retarded the spark by using another lever on the quadrant.

The car has acetylene headlamps, Dietz combination electric-kerosene side-lamps, and a combination tail-lamp. There is no acetylene tank on the car, but on the left running-board is a toolbox that may have contained such a tank. A battery box is on the right running-board. A muffler cut-out pedal is located between the brake and clutch pedals, and there is a starter button in the center of the floorboard just in front of the seats. Mounted on the outside of the body to the right of the driver seat are a siren, with a switch, and a rubber bulb for sounding the horn, which is secured to the body at the right of the dash, below the side-lamp.

The intake-valve side (at top) and the exhaust-valve side of the 1912 Simplex engine.

The controls and instruments of the 1912 Simplex. No provision was made for a windshield.

The 1912 Simplex required a 40-gallon gasoline tank because its fuel consumption was high and gas stations were few; and it required a 13-gallon oil tank because the oil was not recirculated after it was used once.

Instruments on the dash include a Standard Foxboro air-pressure gauge for the gasoline and oil tanks, Weston ammeter, Bosch ignition switch, and a Warner Auto Meter (speedometer) that was driven by gearing on the right front wheel. A handle on the steering column is connected to the cable-controlled choke of the carburetor.

In 1949 the car was completely repainted in red with black striping and reupholstered in pleated black leather by Haley's, Incorporated, an automobile dealer in Washington, D.C., through the courtesy of George C. Hane, owner of the firm. At the same time the seven old tires and inner tubes were replaced with new ones contributed by Harvey S. Firestone, Jr.

Pierce-Arrow

1912
Gift of Arthur V. Lyons in 1965

This 3-passenger, 6-cylinder runabout, an automobile of exceptional quality, was built by the Pierce-Arrow Motor Car Company, of Buffalo, New York, and sold for $4,000. Pierce-Arrow was one of the pioneer producers of 6-cylinder engines. The Museum's car, equipped with a 36-horsepower engine, was known as the "6-36."

The engine has a 4-inch bore, a 5⅛-inch stroke, and a displacement of 386 cubic inches. T-head cylinders are cast in pairs, with heads integral. The intake valves are on the right and the exhaust valves on the left. Valves operate directly from the independent camshafts. The cylinders are mounted on a two-piece crankcase made of cast aluminum alloy and divided on the center line of the motor bearings. The crankcase is attached to the frame at four points by means of two drop-forged steel girders, one at each end of the engine.

Lines from an oil tank located above the left side of the engine run to the timing gears and the seven main bearings that support the hollow crankshaft of chrome-nickel steel. A sight-tube on the dash indicates the level of oil in the tank. Oil circulates through lines bored in the webs supporting the main bearings, where it enters the hollow crankshaft and is carried to the rod bearings and then to the wrist-pins and cylinder walls. An oil pump, located at the left side of the lower crankcase and driven from the exhaust camshaft, returns the oil to the tank. The intake and delivery lines are equipped with wire-gauze strainers.

A centrifugal water pump on the left side of the engine circulates the water from the honeycomb radiator. This pump operates by means of a gear driven by the exhaust timing gears. Between the water pump and the drive gear is an air compressor for pumping up the tires; it is operated by a sliding gear on the water pump shaft. At the rear of the water pump shaft is a coupling for a generator, should one have been desired.

The carburetor, of Pierce-Arrow design, is located on the right side of the engine. Water from the cooling system circulated through the carburetor to heat it, and a tube that leads around

The 1912 Pierce-Arrow.

the rear of the engine to the exhaust pipe on the left side took in the heated air.

The engine is equipped with two separate ignition systems; it carries one set of spark plugs over the cylinders and another set on the right side. One set used a Bosch magneto, gear-driven from the intake timing gears, and the other set operated from a battery and commutator working in conjunction with six coils and a master vibrator. The commutator was driven by a bevel gear from the intake camshaft.

The selective sliding transmission provided four forward speeds and a reverse. The high speed was by direct drive from the engine. The friction-type clutch is an aluminum cone, fitted with a leather facing having cork inserts, that engaged the beveled inner face of the flywheel. The cone also is fitted with a brake which—to facilitate the changing of the gears—automatically brings it to rest when disengaged. Power was transmitted to the semifloating rear axle by means of a drive shaft equipped with two universal joints.

Two braking systems acted on the rear-wheel drums. A pedal operated expanding brake shoes of German bronze, and a lever operated contracting shoes lined with asbestos fabric on a foundation of woven wire.

The controls are situated on the right side of the car. There is a clutch pedal to the left, a brake pedal to the right, and an accelerator pedal between. Near the center of the floor is a pedal for operating a muffler cut-out. To the driver's right are two levers; the one nearest him is the gear-change lever, and the other operated the external brakes. The upper of two levers on the steering column is an additional carburetor control; the lower lever controls spark.

To aid in starting, there is a priming pump, fitted with a pressure gauge, on the dash; it fed gasoline directly to the intake manifold. Also on the dash are a Hoffecker speedometer; a box containing six coils, a vibrator, and the ignition switch; and a Flash Auto-Lighter for electrically igniting the 12-inch headlamps, which are illuminated by gas from a Prest-O-Lite tank hidden in a compartment at the rear of the car. The side-lamps and tail-lamp are the combination type, using either oil or electricity. The small license plate light on the rear is electric, as are the several dash-lights. An electric Klaxon horn is mounted on the left side of the body.

The frame is suspended on semielliptic springs in front and ¾-elliptic springs in the rear. Except for its pressed-aluminum fenders and brass hood (which is fitted with cylinder locks on both sides), the body is of cast aluminum. The rear deck conceals a folding rumble seat. The top half of the windshield can be folded down or slanted outward, and beneath the windshield are two ventilating louvres with screw-operated shutters.

The wooden wheels carry 36-by-4½-inch clincher tires on demountable rims, and two spare tires are mounted on the right running-board. There is a tool compartment in the left apron, just above the running-board, and the gasoline tank is under the seat. Low on the left side of the body is a brass plate which bears the number 32813 for both motor and car.

Ford

1913

Gift of Harvey Carlton Locke in 1935

Probably the best-known and most-talked-about automobile in the world is the famous Model-T Ford. The model first appeared late in 1908 and it continued to be produced, with only minor changes, for almost 19 years. During this period the number of Model-T Fords built was approximately the same as the total number for all other American cars combined—15 million. The Museum's Model-T, bearing engine number 211098, was purchased new for $600 in Rochester, New York, on April 4, 1913, by the donor's father. In the ensuing 22 years it was driven slightly less than 54,000 miles.

The engine is a 4-cylinder, 4-cycle, water-cooled, L-head unit of 3¾-inch bore and 4-inch stroke. Its rated horsepower was 22.5, and it actually developed 20 horsepower at 1,600 revolutions per minute. The block and crankcase are made in one casting. The crankshaft is supported in three bearings, as is the camshaft, which mechanically operated the eight valves. The carburetor is of the constant-level type. The water-jacketed cylinder head is cast separately—an early use of this type of design.

In this particular car the cooling water was circulated by thermosyphon action, but the first several thousand Model-T Fords built in 1908 had centrifugal water pumps. A belt-driven fan is mounted behind the radiator at the front of the car.

The oil pan, or lower half of the crankcase, is of pressed steel and extends back to enclose the bottom of the flywheel, the planetary transmission, and the universal joint. Completing the enclosure is another piece of pressed steel bolted to the top of the extension.

The magneto consists of permanent magnets, bolted to the forward face of the flywheel in a circle close to its rim, and a series of flat, insulated coils supported on a stationary spider in a circle opposite the magnets. As the flywheel revolved, the magnets passed the coils and generated current at about six volts. The current was supplied through a low-tension timer to four trembler coils which increased the voltage for ignition.

The planetary transmission, attached to the back of the flywheel, provided two speeds forward and a reverse. The low-speed and reverse gears and the drum of the foot brake have spring-steel bands faced with friction lining. The high-speed clutch is composed of a number of steel disks. All these parts are fully enclosed in the oil-tight, pressed-steel case. The rotation of the flywheel supplied oil to the engine and the transmission.

The halves of the rear-axle housing, made of pressed steel, are joined in the vertical center plane of the differential housing. Roller bearings support the axle shafts at the inner and outer ends of each half of the housing. Angular braces connect the outer ends of the axle housing to the forward end of a torque tube enclosing the drive shaft, and the axle housing is stiffened by a truss rod (not original equipment) that runs beneath it.

Transverse semielliptic springs (one at front and one at rear) are linked to the axles. Their centers are firmly held in and clipped to the frame's U-shaped front and rear cross members, which are curved to fit the spring arches. Front-axle alignment is maintained by diagonal braces that connect the ends of the axle to the front of the flywheel housing. A muffler extends along the right side of the pressed-steel frame.

Detailed view of the controls, instruments, and coil box of the 1913 Ford. Only the hand brake, three pedals, and simple ignition switch were provided at the factory; all other items are accessories.

The driver controlled the two forward speeds with the left pedal, the reverse with the center pedal, and the transmission brake with the right pedal. He used a lever to operate the expanding brake bands that acted on the rear-wheel drums. When the driver pulled the lever halfway back the left pedal depressed without engaging the brakes, and this put the transmission in neutral position, with neither the low-speed gear nor the high-speed clutch engaged. To engage low speed he depressed the left pedal completely; and to engage high speed he released both the pedal and the lever. A spark-control lever and throttle lever are within easy reach below the steering wheel.

The steering-gear box is of the planetary type and is located within the hub of the steering wheel. An arm at the lower end of the steering column, on the left side of the car, passes over to

The Museum's 1913 Ford after it was reconditioned in 1956.

the right steering knuckle on the front axle. A tie rod connects the two steering knuckles.

The car has a 100-inch wheelbase and a 56-inch tread; it weighs slightly more than 1,200 pounds. The wooden-spoke wheels are mounted with clincher tires—30-by-3-inch on the front wheels and 30-by-3½-inch on the rear. The touring-style body is made of wood and metal; its seats are upholstered with tufted black leather. There is a door on either side at the rear, but the front has a single door, on the right side opposite the driver. The regular equipment included a folding windshield, collapsible top, bulb horn, John W. Brown kerosene tail-lamp, and a pair of E. and J. kerosene side-lamps. The gasoline tank is beneath the front seat. No provision was made for carrying a spare tire.

Many accessories were available for the Model-T Ford. The Museum's car is fitted with a Ward-Leonard electric starting motor, Ward-Leonard electric generator, Stewart and Clark speedometer, New Haven clock, pedal accelerator, Anderson intake manifold, running-board toolbox and battery box, special coil box made by the K-W Ignition Company, Hoyt ammeter, rear-view mirror, hand-operated windshield wiper, and a pair of electric headlights made by John W. Brown. Also, antirattling devices are fitted to the brake rods and steering rods.

In 1954 four new tires and inner tubes (contributed by Harvey S. Firestone, Jr.) were installed, and in 1956 the car was thoroughly cleaned, refurbished, and repainted by National Auto Top Company of Washington, D. C., through the courtesy of Ford Motor Company.

Commercial Electric Truck

1913
Gift of Curtis Publishing Company in 1964

During the early period of motor drayage many commercial houses were opposed to gasoline-powered vehicles, which they considered troublesome to maintain and difficult to operate. Consequently, a number of such firms preferred electric trucks, which offered the drivers an easy transition from horse to motor truck. The Museum's 7-ton electric truck was built by Commercial Truck Company of America, in Philadelphia, where it was used by Curtis Publishing Company from 1913 until 1963.

The truck has four General Electric 16-ampere, 85-volt motors, one geared to each wheel. The front and rear axle assemblies are nearly identical. The motors hang by vertical trunnions, which permitted 4-wheel steering if the purchaser desired that

The Museum's 1913 Commercial electric truck originally had a three-bow top over the driver seat.

View of front-axle assembly of the Commercial truck, showing one motor and steering mechanism.

his truck be so equipped. The Museum's truck does not carry this equipment. Power was transmitted from each motor by means of a double spur-gear train that meshes with an internal gear bolted to the wheel. On rear wheels, the outer surface of the internal gear served as the brake drum for the external contracting brake. The gearing ran in a lubricant. Whenever a motor became defective, that motor and its gearing could be disconnected quickly and the vehicle could operate temporarily on the other motors.

The axles are formed of two square, forged members with a cross-bracing between, thus forming a deep I-beam section. The wheel spindles are fitted with tapered roller bearings. Semielliptic springs of silico-manganese, oil-treated steel rest on the axle assemblies.

Suspended from the body is a large box (with removable covers on both sides) containing 42 lead-type batteries that could drive the vehicle from 20 to 25 miles, on one charging, at a maximum speed of only six miles an hour.

The trussed, channel-sectioned frame is braced with corner gussets, riveted in place. The planked floor of the staked body is covered with a quarter-inch steel plate.

The wooden wheels now carry 10-by-36-inch solid rubber tires, but originally they were equipped with 36-by-5-inch dual tires.

The wide tire surface, together with the 4-wheel drive, gave exceptionally good traction, and the manufacturers guaranteed that the trucks could negotiate more than a foot of snow without chains or other tractive devices.

Beneath the floorboard in the driver's section is a compartment that is accessible through a trap-door at the front of the truck. The headlights are set into this door. Within the compartment are the controller, the lower section of the steering column, an ampere-hour meter, fuses, and switch for the headlights. The controller, surrounding the lower portion of the steering column, is of the continuous-torque type, having four points for forward and two for reverse.

The controls are very simple. The operator turned on the current by inserting a bronze, D-shaped clip into a receptacle to the left of his seat. The truck moved forward when he turned counterclockwise a hand wheel (slightly smaller than the steering wheel) on the vertical steering column just beneath the steering wheel. When he turned this smaller wheel clockwise from neutral the truck ran in reverse. The only other control is a brake pedal that could be set in position by means of a ratchet plate.

Since the driver seat is located above the forward end of the cargo platform, all but 18 inches of the truck's length could be utilized for carrying the load.

Harley-Davidson Motorcycle

1913
Gift of Paul Edward Garber in 1947

The Museum's 1913 Harley-Davidson, bearing engine number 4336-D and known as the Model 9-B, "5-35" (5 horsepower; 35 cubic inches displacement), originally sold for $235 at the factory in Milwaukee, but it was purchased secondhand in 1918 by the donor, who used it for several years. It was restored in 1947 by the Harley-Davidson Motor Company.

The 1-cylinder, 4-cycle, air-cooled engine has a 3⁵⁄₁₆-inch bore and a 4-inch stroke. The cylinder casting and its integral head are of heat-treated gray iron, and the heat-treated, ground piston is fitted with three rings and a hollow steel wrist pin. An I-beam section of chrome-vanadium steel, fitted at both ends with phosphor-bronze bushings, serves as the connecting rod. Separate camshafts for the intake and exhaust valves are driven by gears in the magneto drive train. The overhead intake valve is of

The 1913 Harley-Davidson motorcycle.

Paul Garber astride the 1913 Harley-Davidson motorcycle he presented to the Museum.

nickel steel; and the exhaust valve has a cast-iron head and a nickel-steel stem. The crankcase is of polished aluminum, and the hardened, tool-steel crankshaft is mounted in the crankcase on phosphor-bronze bearings. The crankcase has an oil-drain plug and an overflow pipe.

Ignition was effected by a Bosch high-tension magneto with spark plug, and the fuel was vaporized by a constant-level, float-equipped Schebler carburetor. A priming petcock is in the left side of the cylinder head. A compartmented tank, with one section for gasoline and the other for oil, is mounted at the upper bars of the frame, above the engine. On top of each compartment of the tank are a filler cap and a shut-off metering valve. The oil for the engine passed by gravity through a sight glass into the crankcase. The driver controlled the spark timing by twisting the grip of the left handlebar; and he controlled the throttle opening by twisting the right grip.

The loop-type frame of brazed tubing forms a cradle that supports and protects the motor. The handlebars are tubular, and the steering fork is fitted with both main and recoil springs. A narrow, metal toolbox is mounted vertically on the frame below the saddle, and the curved exhaust pipe culminates in a muffler below the toolbox. The wheels, with wire spokes and metal rims, originally carried 28-by-2½-inch clincher tires, but 28-by-3-inch tires (contributed by Harvey S. Firestone, Jr.) were installed when the motorcycle was restored in 1947. The wheelbase is 57 inches.

The drive was furnished by a double-reduction roller chain (covered by metal guards) that runs from a sprocket on the engine crankshaft to a sprocket at the hub of the rear wheel. The driver operated the clutch, which is on the rear-wheel hub, by means of a lever on the left side of the machine. He engaged the clutch by moving the lever forward.

A pedal-and-chain drive, on the right side, incorporates a New Departure coaster brake. With the rear wheel raised free by the stand and with the clutch engaged, the driver used the pedals to crank the motor. He engaged the brake by a slight backward pressure on the pedals. The pedals were not driven by the forward motion of the machine, but they could be used for propulsion in an emergency, in which case the clutch would be disengaged.

Pope Motorcycle

1913

Gift of Mr. and Mrs. William L. Conners in 1964

This motorcycle was purchased late in 1913 by John R. Beattie of New Haven, Connecticut, the father of Mrs. William L. Conners, a co-donor. The machine was used by Mr. Beattie for about eight years; it then was placed in storage where it remained until it came to the Museum in 1964. Built by the Pope Manufacturing Company of Westfield, Massachusetts, it was known as the Model L and sold for $250.

The two-cylinder engine, bearing the number 246, is secured to the frame at four points. It is rated as having between seven and eight horsepower, although a chart of its performance in tests by the Worcester Polytechnic Institute shows that at 50 miles per hour it developed 15.4 horsepower, with 13.9 horsepower delivered to the rear wheel. The $3\frac{21}{64}$-inch bore and $3\frac{1}{2}$-inch stroke give a displacement of 61 cubic inches. The vehicle's maximum speed was between 60 and 65 miles an hour.

The gray-iron cylinders have separate heads containing nickel-steel valves operated by rocker arms attached to the heads. The intake and exhaust valves are interchangeable. The camshaft and the roller-bearing connecting rods are of nickel steel; the main bearings are of phosphor bronze; and the crankcase is of aluminum.

An oil tank having a capacity of two quarts is compartmented with a toolbox beneath the seat. A mechanically operated oiler, worm-and-gear-driven from the motor shaft, supplied oil from the tank to the top of the crankcase. A spur from the main oil line leads to the front cylinder, thus insuring equal distribution of oil to both cylinders and overcoming the movement of the main body of oil toward the rear while the machine was running forward. A window in the left side of the crankcase shows the oil level. An auxiliary hand pump at the side of the oil tank could be used to supply extra oil for hard pulling or high-speed operation.

A Schebler carburetor is located on the right side of the engine. Ignition was furnished by a Bosch magneto that was shaft-driven from the motor shaft through a worm-and-gear drive.

The gas tank has two sections, each with a capacity of a

119

The 1913 Pope motorcycle.

gallon and a half. Fuel lines and shut-offs are arranged so that the sections may be used independently or as one tank. The fuel line leading to the engine is equipped with a small gauze strainer.

The muffler runs beneath the oil tank; it has a pedal-operated cut-out at the rear.

The driving mechanism consists of a chain running from the engine sprocket to the larger sprocket of the clutch assembly, a chain from a smaller sprocket of the clutch assembly to a sprocket on the left of the rear wheel, and a chain from a sprocket on the right of the rear wheel to a sprocket on the pedal shaft. The latter chain operated the Corbin Duplex V-band brake when backward pressure was applied to the pedals, and it put the machine in motion when forward pressure was applied. When sufficient forward speed had been attained the engine was started by engaging the Eclipse multiple-disk clutch, which was controlled by a hand lever on the left side.

The handlebars have a twin stem as a safety feature. The

right grip controlled the carburetor and the left grip served as a compression release by controlling the opening of the exhaust valves. A small lever on the right side of the gas tank served as the spark control. The ignition switch is mounted on the right handlebar.

The front hub is a ball-bearing type by Corbin. The wheels carry 28-by-3-inch clincher tires. Suspension is by a leaf spring at the front and twin coil springs at the rear. The saddle is of Troxel manufacture. Wheelbase is 56½ inches.

Additional equipment consists of a bulb horn, front and rear acetylene lights having a separate acetylene generator, a Corbin-Brown speedometer geared to the rear wheel, and a luggage rack over the rear fender. The cylindrical toolbox now on the rear fender is an added attachment introduced by the Pope Manufacturing Company in 1915.

This cycle was restored in 1966 by Dale C. Price of Cambridge, Maryland. New tires were installed to replace the missing originals, and the horn and acetylene generator, also missing, were replaced with appropriate types from the Museum's collection. It is possible that the acetylene gas originally may have been furnished from a Prest-O-Lite tank rather than a generator.

Rauch and Lang Electric Automobile

1914

Gift of Mrs. William C. Gorgas in 1929

This car was built when the popularity of the electric automobile was at its peak. Its roomy interior, comfortable ride, and quiet, smooth operation made it especially suitable for city driving and for short trips with frequent stops. Dual controls allowed operation from either the front or rear seat. The car was produced by the Rauch and Lang Carriage Company of Cleveland, Ohio, and it was owned originally by Surgeon General William C. Gorgas.

The designer, John H. Hertner, claimed that the car could travel 100 miles on a single charge of the batteries when it was run at the optimum speed of 13 miles an hour. The top speed was 19 miles an hour, but the range per charge became progressively shorter as the speed was increased beyond the optimum.

The frame consists of two parallel channel-sectioned side members and seven cross members. The 2½-horsepower motor, rated at 80 volts, is suspended from two cross members near the center of the frame and is connected to the worm-driven rear axle by a short drive shaft having two universal joints and a slip joint.

The floating-type rear-axle assembly forms a complete unit. The center section of the housing holds the complete differential mechanism, including the worm and worm wheel. The two end sections—bolted to the center section—enclose the axle shafts, which have splined ends fitted into the differential unit. A torque bar, lying directly beneath the propeller shaft, is connected to the lower front of the differential housing by a tapered joint and to the motor by a universal joint.

Two ⅞-elliptic springs support the frame over the rear-axle assembly. The forward end of the lower half of each spring is connected to a spring bracket at the side of the frame. The springs' eyes are fitted with bronze bushings; the bolts are hardened and ground and have grease cups.

Internal, expanding-type brakes on the rear wheels were operated by pedal (front or rear), with each pedal having a ratchet that enabled the driver to lock it in the depressed position.

Two conventional semielliptic springs are on the tubular front

The 1914 Rauch and Lang electric automobile.

axle. The front wheels turn on individual steering knuckles connected by a tie-rod, and the drag link, which is connected to the left steering knuckle, could be operated by either steering bar.

The car weighs about 4,000 pounds. It has a 54-inch tread, a wheelbase of approximately 100 inches, and wooden-spoke wheels mounted with 36-by-4-inch tires of solid rubber.

A controller handle (at the left of each seat) contracted an external brake on the motor shaft when it was pulled back, and it controlled the motor's speed when it was moved forward. To reverse the motor, the driver depressed a pedal and, at the same time, operated the controller handle for the desired speed. Each controller handle has a built-in cylinder lock. A Stewart-Warner speedometer is within view of the driver.

A compartment beneath the rear-seat cushion now contains a set of tire chains and a Weston voltmeter-ammeter instrument that indicated the state of charge and the rate of charge and discharge of the batteries. The voltmeter scale ranges from zero to 120 volts, and the ammeter scale ranges from plus-50 to minus-150 amperes.

The enclosed body seats four persons—two in the rear and two on individual seats in front. Head room is a few inches less than five feet. Centered on each side is a door with a window glass that can be raised and lowered. The glass of the other two windows on each side is fixed in place, but the windshield and the glass of the window at the rear can be raised and lowered. The seven windows and the windshield are fitted with roller shades, and the windshield has a glass visor. Each door can be locked from the outside by means of a cylinder lock, and from the inside by a thumb screw on the door handle. The interior has a lamp and a flower vase.

The car carries 45 single-cell storage batteries—30 in the front compartment and 15 in the rear compartment. Both compartments have hinged covers. The fenders and running-boards are fitted to the body. The car has a pair of headlamps, a pair of two-directional side-lamps, and a tail-lamp.

White Bus

1917

Gift of Baltimore Transit Company in 1965

This 15-passenger bus, purchased at a cost of about $4,000 in 1917 by a subsidiary of the present Baltimore Transit Company, was used on the Charles Street line in Baltimore until 1922. The body, which was built by J. G. Brill Company, of Philadelphia, is mounted on a chassis of the White Company's 1½-ton truck, Model TBC.

The driver seat and three two-passenger seats are on the left side; and there are two single-passenger seats toward the right front, a longitudinal three-passenger seat toward the right rear, and a four-passenger seat across the back. The center section of the latter seat is removable for access to an emergency door. The seats are covered with woven cane and have corner handles for standees. The bus was entered at the right front through a folding door equipped with a folding step. Front and side windows slide upward and are secured by twin catches on both sides of the sash.

The clutch and brake pedals are in conventional positions, and the accelerator pedal is to the right of the brake. A lever to the driver's left operated the emergency brake, and one to his right changed gears of the selective 4-speed transmission. The gear-change lever, equipped with a button-operated catch, moves in an H-pattern that begins with first speed in the forward right position; reverse is forward of the first-speed position. The spark- and gas-control levers are mounted on the upper end of the steering column, and their movements were transmitted through a pair of bevel gears on the lower end of the column. A pedal operates the wet-plate clutch; the brake pedal contracts shoes on the rear-wheel drums; and the brake lever operates expanding shoes within the drums. The driver controlled the folding door and step by means of a hand crank on a vertical shaft at his left.

On the dash are an ammeter and a number of electrical switches that control various accessories, but none of this equipment was supplied with the original chassis. The Brill Company probably installed some of the accessories when it built the body, and other items may have been added in later years. Such accessories include five dome lights and a ceiling buzzer that could be operated by any of a number of push-buttons on the upright posts of the body frame. The present horn is electric, but the original supposedly was a hand-operated Klaxon. Illumination originally was provided by a pair of headlamps supplied with acetylene from a Prest-O-Lite tank, a pair of Adlake side-lamps that used oil, and an oil tail-lamp. The side-lamps have been electrified, and the other lamps have been replaced by electric ones.

The 4-cylinder engine has a 3¾-inch bore and a 5⅛-inch stroke and is rated at 22.5 horsepower. It is cast *en bloc* with manifolds integral. A gear train across the front of the engine operated the timing gear, camshaft, water-pump, fan, and magneto. When the Museum received the bus, the original water pump had been replaced by one driven by a separate

The body of this 1917 motor bus is mounted on a chassis of a 1½-ton White truck.

electric motor, and the original carburetor, made by the White Company, had been replaced by a Zenith. Ignition was provided by a high-tension Bosch magneto, above which has been added a combination starter-generator (made by North East Electric Company) driven by silent chain from the magneto shaft below. Originally, the hand crank (still in place) was used for starting.

Lubrication was by a combination method of pressure and splash, with the oil pump located in the upper right side of the crankcase. The oil supply was carried in a cast-aluminum well near the right rear of the engine. Oil level in the crankcase could be checked by pulling a knob to the right of the starting crank; oil would then drip out if it were at the proper level.

The cellular-type radiator is supported on both sides by spring type shock absorbers that protect it from excessive jarring.

In the original White chassis the gas tank was under the operator's seat and the fuel system was of the gravity type; however, body design of the bus necessitated different arrangement. The tank is now under the body, on the right side, and the fuel is supplied to the engine by means of a Stewart vacuum gasoline system.

The frame is of heat-treated, pressed alloy steel; its side members are of quarter-inch steel, six inches high.

Power was transmitted to the wheels by a plain-bevel, double-reduction axle of White Company manufacture. The front axle is a heat-treated forging of alloy steel, I-beam in section. Both axles are secured to the frame by semielliptic springs. Propulsion is taken by a pair of radius rods secured to the frame's side members.

The rear wheels, of wood construction, are built up with two thicknesses of soft, cushion rubber in the rims to absorb shocks. They have a gauge of 66 inches and carry 36-by-7-inch tires of solid rubber. The front wheels, with a gauge of 58½ inches, are of cast steel and carry 34-by-4-inch solid rubber tires. Wheelbase is 157½ inches.

Oldsmobile

1918
Gift of Robert E. Maytag in 1964

This 4-door, 5-passenger touring car was built by the Olds Motor Works, of Lansing, Michigan, and originally sold for $1,185. It is an Oldsmobile Model 37 bearing serial number 153041 and motor number D-3363.

The 6-cylinder engine, cast *en bloc* and rated at 19 horsepower, has a $2^{13}/_{16}$-inch bore and a $4\frac{3}{4}$-inch stroke. It was lubricated by a force-feed system and was cooled by a water pump (on the left side) that circulated water through a cellular radiator capped by a Monitor temperature gauge.

Oldsmobile Model 37, of 1918.

A Stewart vacuum gasoline system supplied the Johnson carburetor with fuel carried in a tank at the rear.

A 6-volt battery under the right front seat furnished current to the Delco electrical system. In addition to the standard lighting equipment are two spotlights, one mounted on each side of the windshield.

A cone-type clutch and a selective, sliding-type transmission, having three forward speeds and reverse, transmitted power to the full-floating rear axle through spiral bevel gears. Both front and rear springs are of the semielliptic type. Propulsion and torque were through the rear springs—the Hotchkiss system.

The car's wheelbase is 112 inches and its tread 56 inches. The wooden wheels have demountable rims and carry 32-by-4-inch tires. A spare tire is mounted on the rear.

Equipment on the dash consists of a Stewart speedometer, clock, ammeter, lighting and ignition switches, and choke control. A horn button and spark and throttle levers are above the steering wheel. Clutch, service brake, and accelerator pedals are in conventional positions; the gear-change lever is in the center of the floor and the emergency brake lever is to its right. The service brake contracts on rear-wheel drums; the emergency brake expands within the drums.

Model of Liberty Truck

1918
Transferred from the United States War Department

This nonoperable model (scale approximately 1:7) represents the Army's so-called Liberty Truck, which officially was termed the Standardized Class B Truck. It was rated as having from three to five tons carrying capacity.

Even prior to the entry of the United States into World War I, military men foresaw the advantages of having several standardized types of vehicles rather than dozens of different commercial models. Accordingly, in early fall of 1917, about 50 automotive engineers from various truck and parts manufacturing companies met in Washington to design a vehicle in accordance with Army specifications. Parts for the trucks were

Model of Liberty Truck, 1918.

made by the various parts manufacturers and sent to the truck manufacturers for final assembly. In early October, less than a month after the drawings were completed, two sample Class B trucks were running, but the first lot of trucks did not roll off a production line until March of the following year. Large shipments overseas were not made until midsummer, and generally these arrived too late to take an active part in the war operations. About 18,000 Liberty Trucks were built, and although they were too late to assist the war effort they performed admirably and the interest shown in them focused the attention of engineers on improvements in truck design and probably accelerated the development of motor freight carriers.

The full-size truck had a 4-cylinder engine of the L-head type with cylinders cast in pairs and separate heads for each pair. The 4¾-by-6-inch bore and stroke gave a horsepower rated at 36.1, and could develop 58 horsepower at 1,350 revolutions per minute. The best features of Continental, Waukesha, Wisconsin, Buda, and Hercules engines were incorporated in the design of this engine. An oil pump at the right rear of the crankcase provided pressure lubrication throughout the engine. A governor on the engine limited the speed of the truck to 14 miles an hour. The carburetor, like the engine, is of a composite design. Each cylinder had two spark plugs, one operating from a magneto and the other from a battery.

The engine was cooled by a vertical-tube radiator, a centrifugal pump, and a 22-inch fan. The water system, with a capacity of 12 gallons, had 35,000 square inches of cooling surface. The radiator shell was cast, and the entire unit was protected by a sturdy guard mounted on the front of the frame.

The sliding-gear transmission, with unusually wide gears, had four forward speeds and a reverse. First speed and reverse had a ratio of 5.93:1; high speed was by direct drive. The dry, multiple-disk clutch, containing 18 plates, was enclosed in a bell housing.

Gasoline was carried in two 16-gallon tanks, one under the seat and one on the dash. The fuel in the underseat tank was sent to the dash tank by means of a hand pump on the front corner of the right seat. The carburetor was gravity-fed from the tank on the dash.

The truck had Hotchkiss drive, both drive and torque being taken by the rear springs. The rear axle was of the full-floating, single-reduction type, and final drive was by worm gear. The bevel-gear differential was of the free-acting type, though the Army had originally preferred the locking type.

Most early Class B trucks had wooden wheels, but all later ones had cast-steel wheels with seven hollow spokes, as on the Museum's model. The tires were of solid rubber, the front ones

36 by 5 inches and the dual ones on the rear 40 by 6 inches. Both service and emergency brakes, of the internal-expanding type, were located in rear-wheel drums.

The truck's springs were of the semielliptic type. The front springs measured 44 by 3 inches and had 12 leaves; the rear ones, 58 by 4 inches, had 20 leaves.

Illumination was provided by a pair of 21-candlepower head-lamps mounted on the dash; a pair of 2-candlepower side-lamps (for use near combat areas) mounted on the front-bumper sup-ports; a tail-lamp; an instrument lamp; and a trouble lamp that plugged into a socket on the instrument board.

The steering column was nearly vertical. Controls consisted of a brake pedal to the right of the steering column and a clutch pedal to the left; an accelerator pedal to the right of the brake pedal; gear-change and emergency brake levers on the opera-tor's right; and a hand throttle and spark-control lever on the right side of the steering column. On many of these trucks there was a lever (to the left of the driver) for raising and lowering a sprag that trailed behind, as a safety brake, when the vehicle was ascending steep grades. The seat, built to carry four per-sons, has the rather unusual feature of the driver's position being second from the left.

In addition to the Class B truck, the engineers also designed two lighter trucks, the Class A, and Class AA. Sample models of these were built, but neither truck was ever put into production.

German children in a Class B (Liberty) Truck at Mayen, Germany, in December 1918.

Autoped Motor Scooter

1918
Gift of Lawrence Bourgeois in 1964

This lightweight scooter was built in 1918 by the Autoped Company of America, Long Island City, New York. It bears the number D3201 on the left side of the engine.

The 4-cycle engine, mounted on the left side of the front wheel, has an air-cooled integral-head cylinder bolted to a circular crankcase. In front of the cylinder is a breather tube that protrudes from the top of the crankcase; the carburetor and muffler are behind the cylinder. The Breeze carburetor has a screw-adjusted air intake, and its needle valve is operated by a small knob bearing numbers for convenience in adjustment. A shutter serves as a throttle control. On the side of the intake manifold is a small priming cup. The intake valve is automatic and the exhaust valve is cam operated. The engine is geared to the wheel by means of a disk clutch.

The flywheel, on the right side of the front wheel, contains a 6-volt lighting generator that originally furnished current for lighting and ignition, but the system later was altered by the addition of an ignition coil and four dry-cell batteries. The ignition switch is mounted on the right side of the frame, and the gasoline tank is above the front fender.

All control of the vehicle is through the steering column. Turning the column steered the machine in the conventional manner; pushing it forward engaged the clutch; and pulling it back operated the internal, expanding brake on the front wheel. Turning the left grip operated the throttle, and turning the right grip operated the compression release through a wire controlling the opening and closing of the intake valve. A hand Klaxon is mounted on the left grip. The steering column can be folded down and secured to the rear fender for compactness in storage.

Illumination was provided by a headlamp, mounted at the right of the front wheel, and a tail-lamp.

The operator stood on rubber pads on the frame of the vehicle. A two-pronged stand, attached to the underside of the frame, was operated by means of a pedal that extends through the floor. A utility box, mounted toward the front of the machine, now contains the batteries that were added to the electrical system; an ignition coil is mounted just in front of the utility box.

The 15-by-2¼-inch pneumatic tires, made expressly for this vehicle by the Empire Rubber and Tire Company, Trenton, New Jersey, bear the inscription "Auto Ped Tire, Empire red, non-skid."

The 1918 Autoped scooter shown with its steering column in driving position and in folded position for storage.

Cleveland Motorcycle

1918
Gift of Richard and Russell Fiedler in 1951

This motorcycle, bearing engine number 5283, cost $175 in 1918 at the Cleveland Motorcycle Company in Cleveland, Ohio. Advertisements of the period claimed this machine could travel 75 miles on a gallon of gasoline and that it had a top speed of from 35 to 40 miles an hour. This make of motorcycle, introduced in August 1915 when the price at the factory was $150, was one of the most popular lightweight motorcycles of the period.

The 2½-horsepower, 1-cylinder, 2-cycle, air-cooled engine has a 2½-inch bore and a 2¾-inch stroke, providing a total piston displacement of 13½ cubic inches. A Brown and Barlow float-feed, single-jet carburetor, with auxiliary air control, is bolted to the inlet port at the front of the cylinder and is controlled by a pair of levers on the right handlebar. The motor is lubricated by a mixture of oil and gasoline in the fuel tank. A Bosch high-tension magneto, with spark plug, supplies the ignition.

The cycle's frame is of heavy-gauge, seamless steel tubing, brazed at the joints; wheelbase is 54 inches. The engine and gear box are secured in the frame by two large suspension bolts. The gear box, which is integral with the aluminum crankcase, contains a set of two-speed sliding gears of chrome-nickel steel, a heat-treated, alloy-steel worm with a titanium-bronze worm gear, and a clutch composed of 13 disks of hardened and ground steel. Low ratio of the gear box is 10 to 1; high ratio, 6.1 to 1. The transmission gears run in an oil bath.

The driver engaged the clutch by moving forward a lever on his left; operated the brake by depressing a pedal with his left foot, which contracted a band on a drum on the left side of the rear wheel; and changed gears by operating a pedal with his right foot. A kick starter is attached to the left side of the gear box. The rear wheel is driven by a roller chain from a sprocket on the output shaft of the transmission, on the right side of the machine. There is no guard over the chain.

The steering fork is fitted with a coil spring and its tubular handlebars have rubber grips. A cylindrical muffler, of cast aluminum, is mounted in front of the crankcase. The wire-

Cleveland motorcycle, 1918.

spoke wheels have metal rims and mount 26-by-2½-inch clincher tires (of the 1920s) that have been equipped with new butyl-rubber inner tubes. Each wheel has a mudguard, and there is a stand at the rear of the frame. A cylindrical fuel tank, equipped with a shut-off valve at the bottom, is suspended from the frame over the engine; and a small, metal toolbox is attached to the rear underside of the tank. The footrests, adjacent to the brake and gear-shift pedals, are rubber-covered. The saddle is a Mesinger "Auto Cushion." The motorcycle has no battery, generator, lighting equipment, or warning signal. Its total weight is about 150 pounds.

In 1951 the motorcycle was disassembled, cleaned, refinished, and reassembled. The 1926 District of Columbia license plate—on the vehicle when it was given to the Museum—was refinished in its original colors.

American-LaFrance Fire Truck

1920
Gift of City of Bristow, Oklahoma, in 1964

The American-LaFrance Fire Engine Company of Elmira, New York, completed this triple-combination fire truck (construction number 2920) for the City of Bristow, Oklahoma, on March 9, 1920. Trucks of this class, designated Type 12 by the manufacturer, were intended primarily for towns and small cities that required, for reasons of economy, a general-purpose fire-fighting vehicle to serve as pumper, chemical truck, and hose truck. The Type 12 was well suited to the needs of Bristow, and it continued in service there until April 1958, making more than 2,000 runs in its 38-year career.

The history of the development of gasoline-propelled fire trucks (a few experimental units were built in the early 1900s) closely parallels that of the motor truck in this country. Their great advantage over horse-drawn steam pumpers was their speed in getting to a fire, which often was half the time required for horse-drawn engines. By 1910 gasoline fire trucks were considered a practical alternative to horse-drawn equipment, and within five years steam pumpers were considered entirely obsolete—although a limited number continued in use for many more years—and all major cities were adopting gasoline-propelled apparatus for fire fighting.

American-LaFrance has a history of fire-apparatus manufacturing that dates back through a complex lineage of predecessor companies to 1845. A pioneering firm in the production of gasoline fire trucks, the company produced its first gasoline pumper in 1910. It is the largest independent maker of fire equipment in the United States, supplying nearly half of all new units purchased by domestic fire companies.

Mechanically, the Type 12 fire truck is conventional in all particulars. The 6-cylinder, T-head, water-cooled engine is rated at 105 horsepower at 1,600 revolutions per minute. The cylinders, cast in pairs, have offset inlet and exhaust valves on opposite sides, and the float-feed carburetor has an automatic auxiliary air intake. Ignition is provided by an Eiseman magneto and an auxiliary battery system. The multiple-disk, dry-plate clutch has asbestos linings, on steel, for friction surfaces. The sliding-gear

An American-LaFrance fire truck similar to the Museum's truck, designated a Type 12 by the manufacturer. (Reproduced from an American-LaFrance catalog.)

transmission provides three forward speeds and reverse. The transmission and differential gear box are cast integral, and the jackshaft of the differential is connected to the rear wheels by roller chains. Maximum speed is 50 miles per hour.

A rotary gear pump, located under the driver seat, delivered water to the fire hoses at a rate of 750 gallons a minute. It was powered from a secondary gear box bolted to the top of the transmission. The pump's driving gear was disengaged, of course, when the truck was in motion.

A 40-gallon chemical tank, located behind the gasoline tank to the rear of the driver seat, has decorative ends of hammered nickel plate. Other particulars of this class of fire engine are included in the following specification contained in an American-LaFrance catalog of 1923:

Motor: 6 cylinders, with 5½-inch bore and 6-inch stroke; 105 horsepower.
Wheelbase: 156½ inches.
Wheels: Artillery type.
Tires: 36 by 4 inches, single in front and dual in rear; hard-base cushion; pneumatic (or special types furnished at additional cost).
Lighting system: Two 12-inch electric headlights; one 12-inch electric searchlight.

Gasoline tank: Capacity of 30 gallons, gravity feed.
Siren: Hand-operated.
Locomotive bell.
Toolbox.
Equipment box: At rear.
Crowbar.
Water hose: 1,200 feet, 2½-inch.
Chemical tank: Capacity of 40 gallons.
Chemical hose: 200 feet, ¾-inch.
Ladders: 20-foot extension ladder and 12-foot roof ladder with
    folding hooks.
Suction hoses: Two, each 10 feet 6 inches in length.
Pike pole.
Play pipe cones: Two.
Axe: Fire department standard.
Lanterns: Two, Dietz fire department standard.
Extinguishers: Two, 3-gallon Babcock.
Bumper: Heavy steel with recoil springs.

Models of Two Autocar Trucks

1921
Gifts of the Autocar Company in 1922

Quarter-scale, nonoperable models represent two types of 1921 Autocar trucks, the XXVI-B and XXVI-Y. Except for wheelbase and body type the trucks were identical. The XXVI-B had a 156-inch wheelbase and a unit-construction, rack body; the other truck had a 120-inch wheelbase and a rotary dump body with power hoist.

The pressed-steel, channel-section frame, fitted with cross members and braces, was carried on four semielliptic springs. Tread was 63 inches.

The front axle was of drop-forged steel in I-beam section, and the front wheels, mounted on adjustable, tapered, roller bear-

Quarter-scale models of two 1921 Autocar trucks. The Type XXVI-B truck (represented by the model in photo below) had a wheelbase of 156 inches. The dump truck (Type XXVI-Y) had a 120-inch wheelbase.

ings, carried 34-by-5-inch tires of solid rubber. An irreversible steering gear was on the left side of the truck.

The gear-driven rear axle was of the full-floating, double-reduction type, with the gear reduction being compounded through bevel and spur gears. This construction allowed low reduction without loss of road clearance; also, it reduced the angularity of the propeller shaft, giving straight lines for the transmission of power. All gears in the rear axle were of heat-treated steel and were carried on adjustable, tapered, roller bearings. The complete gear train was mounted on a cover plate bolted to the axle housing, but both the gear train and cover plate could be removed as a unit for inspection and adjustment. Since the rear wheels were mounted on adjustable, tapered, roller bearings carried on an extension of the axle housing, the rotating parts of the axle carried no part of the vehicle's weight; their only function was to transmit power to the rear wheels. The driving axles were of heat-treated alloy steel. The 36-by-10-inch tires were of solid rubber.

The engine and clutch comprised a single unit that was suspended from the frame (beneath the seat structure) at three points. The 4-cylinder, 4-cycle, water-cooled engine had a 4¼-inch bore and a 5½-inch stroke and was rated at 28.9 horsepower. Its counterbalanced crankshaft of heat-treated

alloy steel was mounted on two ball bearings.

An automatic, float-equipped carburetor was gravity-fed from a 25-gallon gasoline tank behind the seat. Water was cooled in a vertical-tube radiator in front of a belt-driven fan and was circulated by a centrifugal pump. A high-tension magneto, gear-driven by the engine, provided the ignition.

A camshaft-driven gear pump in the lower engine pan lubricated the engine by supplying oil to jets under the connecting rods, thus insuring a constant level for the connecting-rod dippers under all conditions.

The pedal-controlled, dry-disk clutch had two asbestos-faced driving plates attached to the flywheel and a driven plate attached to the driving shaft.

The selective-type transmission, providing four forward speeds and a reverse, was suspended from the frame at three points and was connected to the clutch by a fabric-disk universal joint. A tubular drive shaft, with a universal joint at each end, transmitted power to the rear axle. All gears and shafts were of heat-treated alloy steel mounted on ball bearings.

Both sets of brakes—service and emergency—were of the internal expanding type that operated on steel drums bolted to the rear wheels. The service brake was operated by a pedal and the emergency (or parking) brake by a lever.

The driver changed vehicle speed by operating a lever to his right, and he controlled engine speed by means of spark and throttle levers on the steering wheel and an accelerator pedal. A governor that was operated by both vehicle speed and engine speed could be set and locked for a predetermined maximum speed.

Gas headlamps were supplied with fuel from an acetylene tank. The tail-lamp burned oil.

Cadillac Chassis

1923
Gift of Cadillac Motor Car Company in 1923

The Smithsonian originally exhibited the chassis of the Model 61 Cadillac of 1923 along with its Model A Cadillac car of 1903 to indicate the many changes made in Cadillac construction over the 20-year period. The Model 61 followed by eight years the production of the first Cadillac having a V-8 engine—the Model 51 of 1915—and its chassis illustrates quality-car construction of its time.

The water-cooled, V-type engine consists of two 4-cylinder blocks with detachable cylinder heads placed at 90-degree angles on an aluminum crankcase. Its 3⅛-inch bore and 5⅛-inch stroke gave a total piston displacement of 314.4 cubic inches, and at 2,700 revolutions per minute it could develop 60 horsepower. The 16 valves were mechanically operated by a single

View of the Cadillac chassis of 1923, as photographed in the same year.

Another view of the 1923 Cadillac chassis.

camshaft located in the center of the engine above the crankshaft, which is supported in three bearings.

A Morse timing chain, at the front of the engine, drove the camshaft, the shaft of the Delco distributor of the battery ignition system, the Delco generator shaft (which lies in the V of the engine), and the water pumps. The generator served also as the starter motor. A starter pedal mechanically engaged the starter gear with a large ring gear on the flywheel (at the rear of the engine) and closed the starter switch. A pivoted weight, turning with the distributor shaft, automatically advanced the ignition timing as higher speeds were reached.

The engine was lubricated both by force-feed and by splash methods. A gear pump, under the front part of the engine, sent oil through passages in the crankshaft. Bolted to the bottom of the crankcase (which has a capacity of six quarts) is an aluminum oil pan that could be removed for access to the engine's lower interior.

Air pressure in a 20-gallon tank at the rear of the car forced gasoline to a constant-level, float-equipped carburetor connected to an intake manifold that branches to both cylinder blocks. While the engine was running, a small engine-driven compressor maintained the air pressure in the tank; with the engine at rest, initial pressure was established by means of a hand pump on the instrument panel.

The intake manifold was heated by the exhaust gases passing through a jacket on the manifold. Each block has its own exhaust manifold, muffler, and water pump. The mufflers run along the center of the chassis, and the water pumps are at the lower front of the engine. The tubular radiator, mounted vertically at the front of the chassis and with a fan behind it, has an overflow pipe that connects with an expansion tank on the right side of the frame. Projecting below the radiator is a crankshaft extension for hand cranking.

The multiple-disk clutch and the transmission, which are directly behind the engine, provided three forward speeds and a reverse, with the selection being made by means of a gear-shift lever (mounted on the gear box) that has a built-in mechanism which allowed it to be locked in the neutral position. On the side of the transmission housing is a small Kellogg air-cooled, 1-cylinder air pump for inflating tires; it was operated by means of an attached lever that engaged the pump's driving gear with one of the transmission gears.

The driver disengaged the clutch by depressing the left pedal and applied the brakes by depressing the right pedal, which is connected by rods to contracting bands on rear-wheel drums. The hand-brake lever, which is pivoted on the outside of the gear box, is attached to rods that connect with expanding shoes within the drums.

The differential unit on the Timkin, full-floating rear-axle assembly is connected to the transmission by a propeller shaft having a Spicer universal joint at each end. The steering wheel, which is on the left side, operated a worm and sector that controlled a tie rod that connects the steering knuckles—one at each end of the front axle. Alemite fittings for lubrication are provided for all shackle bolts, front-axle kingpins, steering parts, and so forth.

The frame, consisting of two U-shaped channels and four cross members, is supported at the front by two semielliptic springs and at the rear by a pair of semielliptic springs and a transverse spring. There are no shock absorbers, but rebound straps are fitted to the outer ends of the rear-axle housing. A torque arm leads from the rear axle to the center cross member of the frame.

The gasoline tank, suspended at the rear between the two side members of the frame, is equipped with an airtight cap and a float-operated gauge on the top rear. Behind the tank is a carrier for a spare rim and tire.

The instrument panel contains gauges for oil and air pressure, a Weston ammeter, a Van Sicklen speedometer, and an Elgin clock.

The chassis has a 132-inch wheelbase and a 56-inch tread, and its Kelsey artillery-type wheels have demountable rims (23 inches in diameter) that carry 33-by-5-inch, straight-side pneumatic tires.

Most parts of the chassis are cross-sectioned, revealing mechanisms seldom seen by the typical owner of an automobile. For identification, all water passages are green, all parts related to the intake and exhaust systems are red, and the frame is white.

Franklin

1924

Gift of Henry W. Mathis in 1962

The Museum's 4-door, 5-passenger Franklin sedan was built by the H. H. Franklin Manufacturing Company, of Syracuse, New York, the only American firm until recent years to successfully market an automobile with an air-cooled engine. Production of the Franklin spanned three decades. The Museum's car, a Model 10-C, cost $2,850 new in 1924. Its manufacturer's plate bears serial number 150305-11, but there is some doubt that the plate is the car's original one.

The 6-cylinder, air-cooled engine, having a 3¼-inch bore and a 4-inch stroke, is rated at 25.35 horsepower. Each cylinder is cast singly, has a nondetachable head, and is surrounded by 52 vertical cooling fins of pressed steel. The in-head valves are operated from the chain-driven camshaft by means of long push-rods acting against rocker arms positioned above the cylinder heads. A force-feed lubrication system supplied oil under pressure to the crankshaft and connecting-rod bearings. Cooling was effected by a squirrel-cage blower (housed in front of the engine) that forced air through a large, bonnet-like, pressed-steel duct over the cylinder heads.

A Stewart vacuum gasoline system supplied fuel to the Stromberg carburetor from a 13½-gallon tank (at the rear) that is equipped with a gauge and with a lever for switching from the regular supply to a reserve gasoline section. Air to the carburetor was filtered through an amply proportioned United air cleaner.

A 6-volt battery beneath the right front seat supplied current for the Atwater-Kent electrical system. The generator, possibly a replacement, was made by the Owen Dyneto Corporation.

Power from the engine passed through a selective sliding transmission providing three forward speeds and reverse. The dry, single-plate clutch was manufactured by Merchant and Evans. The drive shaft is equipped with Spicer universals; and final drive is through spiral bevel gears. Propulsion and torque are taken only on the rear springs.

The semifloating rear axle has a cast housing for the differential and drive gears, and the rear of the housing has a large

The Museum's 1924 Franklin sedan, as photographed in the old Automobile Hall in the Arts and Industries Building.

removable cover plate for easy access to these parts. The front axle is of tubular construction. Full-elliptic springs are mounted near each wheel, and Watson Stabilators serve as snubbers to lessen road shocks. The snubbers are heavy web straps that run from the axle to winding drums attached to the frame.

The sedan's wheelbase is 115 inches and its tread 56 inches. The wooden wheels have demountable rims carrying 32-by-4-inch tires, although the car's specifications called for 32-by-4.95-inch balloon tires.

The brake, clutch, and accelerator pedals are located in conventional positions; the hand-brake lever is to the left of the driver, and the gear-change lever to his right. The pedal-operated service brake contracts on the transmission brake drum; the hand brakes contract on rear-wheel drums.

On the dash are a choke control, spark-adjustment lever, Waltham speedometer and clock, and electric switches for the lights, ignition, and priming mechanism. Beneath the dash is a knob for controlling the vents of a Francisco heater. A horn button and throttle lever are on the steering wheel.

On the driver's side is a vacuum-operated windshield wiper, and on both sides of the forward portion of the body are small ventilators that admit air under the dash. The upper half of the windshield opens outward, and above it on the outside is an adjustable sun visor.

A spare tire is carried on the rear by a three-armed spider that has a detachable clip on one arm for loosening the tire.

The Franklin lion was introduced as a hood ornament on this model.

Army Tractor-Truck

1926

Transferred from the Department of the Army in 1963

This experimental vehicle, possibly the only one of its kind, was designed and built at Camp Holabird, Maryland, about 1926. It was known to the Army as a TTSW (tractor-truck, six-wheel drive). The objective of its designers was to produce a truck that would not put great pressure on subsoil but would have the mobility—so far as possible in a wheeled vehicle—of the track-laying type of vehicle, such as the tank. The Army, which usually under-rated its vehicles, listed it as a 1½-ton truck but it probably was capable of carrying about 6 tons.

The 4-cylinder, 40-horsepower engine (bearing the number 21242) was made by Hinkley Motors, Incorporated, of Ecorse, Michigan. The designers intended to substitute a 6-cylinder engine of from 70 to 80 horsepower, but if this was done the 6-cylinder engine was replaced, in turn, by the present one. The engine is cast *en bloc,* but its cylinder heads are arranged in pairs. Ignition and lighting was provided by a 6-volt Westinghouse system.

The transmission has four forward speeds and a reverse, but a drop gear in the transfer case could double the number of speeds to eight forward and two reverse. The transfer case has three power take-offs but there is no evidence to show how these were used. Originally the truck was equipped with a winch, which undoubtedly was powered from one of the take-offs.

A drive shaft runs from the transmission to the transfer case, from which one shaft runs to the front axle and another to the forward rear axle. Another shaft runs between the two rear axles. All of these shafts are telescoping, a feature that allows irregular wheel movements over uneven terrain. On each axle are a differential and a driving unit. The wheels are driven by internal gears.

The four pairs of wheels on the rear and the single front wheels carry 38-by-7-inch pneumatic tires. The front wheels also carry ten stud bolts for the attachment of second wheels, but duals seldom were used on front during trials. It was reported that the dual front wheels caused steering to be difficult on ordinary roads, and that they made the truck unmanageable on rough terrain.

The truck originally had self-equalized 4-wheel brakes, but these have been removed. Now, the pedal and the lever operate the same brakes, which contract externally on two 9-inch drums on the propeller shaft, one on either end of the transfer case.

The fuel supply is carried in two gasoline tanks—a 20-gallon one under the seat and a 10-gallon one mounted on the dash. A vacuum fuel system is provided.

The cooling system consists of a water pump and a finned-tube radiator of the type used on the Liberty, or Class B, trucks.

On the steering column are an accelerator lever and, just below it, a spark-control lever. Clutch and brake pedals are in conventional positions; the accelerator pedal is to the right of the brake pedal; and a starter pedal is above the brake pedal. In the center of the floor are three hand-controls. The one to the right is the brake lever, and the center one is the gear-change lever. The lever on the left operated three rods that are connected to the transfer case; this lever no longer functions, but it is assumed that it controlled the drop gear and the power take-offs.

On the dash are an ammeter, an oil-pressure gauge, two electrical switches, an instrument light, and a choke knob. The horn button is on the top edge of the body panel, just in front of the door.

The body is 12 feet long, 6 feet 8 inches wide, and 24 inches deep. Five wooden bows support the canvas cover. There was supposedly a draw-bar pull on the rear but now there is no evidence of one.

The TTSW of 1926 as photographed by the Army before deterioration had occurred.

Mack Truck

1930
Gift of Victor Ottilio and Sons in 1963

The Model AC Mack Truck, popularly called the Mack Bulldog, was introduced in 1915 by Mack Trucks, Incorporated, and was produced without major change until 1937. It was manufactured as a regular truck in sizes ranging from 3½ to 7½ tons and as a tractor truck in sizes from 7 to 15 tons. Wheelbases of 156, 168, and 180 inches were available.

The 4-cylinder, 40-horsepower engine in the Museum's truck is cast *en bloc* and has a 5-inch bore and a 6-inch stroke. This type of engine was introduced in 1929; engines in earlier models had cylinders cast in pairs. Suspension, on three points, is accomplished by bolts that pass from overhead beams through the upper crankcase and retain the caps of the front and rear main bearings. Thus, the crankcase itself does not have the burden of supporting the engine. The valves, which have diameters of 1⅞ inches, are on the right side, as are the manifolds, a Stromberg SF-3 carburetor, and governor connections. On the pump and magneto cross-shaft, which is in front of the engine, is a bronze transverse gear driven by the helical camshaft gear. The governor is connected with the nut that retains the camshaft gear; it supposedly is set for an operating speed of 18 miles an hour in high gear. The crankshaft is drop-forged and case-hardened; its main bearings are 3 inches in diameter and its crankpins are 2⅜ inches in diameter.

The single-plate, dry clutch is mounted in the flywheel, and bolted to its cover is a squirrel-cage centrifugal blower that forces air up between the two sections of the radiator, which is in front of the dash. The radiator consists of 154 finned tubes—77 on either side of the truck. Shutters are provided on the outer sides of the radiator's two sections.

The lubrication system is of the circulating splash type, with the oil being fed to the bearings only by gravity, except at high speeds, when the oil pump causes the reservoir to be entirely filled and oil is forced through the leads under direct pump pressure. The oil is pumped to the reservoir by a gear-driven pump operating from a helical gear on the camshaft.

Ignition is supplied by a single high-tension magneto of the inductor or stationary armature type. A brass tube carries the cables from the distributor over the top of the engine, from which individual leads extend to the spark plugs.

The gasoline is gravity fed from a 25-gallon tank under the seat.

Throttle and spark-control levers are mounted on the steering column. The brake pedal, to the right of the clutch pedal, contracts bands on drums at the ends of the jackshaft. An accelerator pedal, with a heel rest behind it, is between the clutch and brake pedals. There are three levers on the driver's right. The first one engages the power take-off; the center one changes the transmission gears; and the third operates expanding brake shoes in rear-wheel drums. Both braking systems are assisted by a vacuum booster, and all brakes can be adjusted, without the use of tools, by self-locking wing nuts. A short lever to the far right is moved horizontally to operate the by-pass valve of the hydraulic hoist.

On the dash are oil-pressure and temperature indicators and the ignition switch. A choke control is under the dash and a similar one is near the starting crank at the front of the truck. The upper half of the removable windshield can be swung upward and outward for ventilation and its single wiper can be operated by vacuum or by hand. The two doors—one on either side of the cab—slide vertically on channels and can be secured

The Museum's Mack Bulldog, which participated in the construction of the famous George Washington Bridge and the Lincoln Tunnel between New York City and New Jersey.

Detailed view of the Mack Bulldog showing the Heil hydraulic hoist, drive chain, and large wing nut for brake adjustment.

in the raised position by a trip-latch. There is an oil lamp on either side of the cab and a hand-operated Klaxon on the left side.

The transmission case and the differential housing are bolted together as a single unit that is suspended from the frame at three points. The transmission's sliding gears are mounted on an interrupted-spline shaft, and the countershaft gears are keyed and pressed in place. The countershaft extends forward through the transmission case, so it can be used as a power take-off. The three higher speeds were for ordinary use; the first gear was used as an emergency low for pulling out of excavations or for driving in sand or snow. The fourth speed is direct drive.

Bevel gears transmitted the power from the transmission to the semifloating jackshafts. The differential, of the 3-pinion bevel-gear type, can be removed as a unit by uncovering the large opening on the back of its housing. A 2-inch-pitch roller chain runs from each of the two 14-tooth sprockets at the outer ends of the jackshafts to the 39-tooth sprockets of the rear wheels.

The pressed channel frame is made of $5/16$-inch heat-treated chrome-nickel steel; its cross members have flared ends and are riveted to the side pieces.

The springs are semielliptic. The rear ones, with 17 leaves, are assisted by short helper springs having four leaves; the front springs have 12 leaves. The axles are forged from one piece of alloy steel. The front axle is of I-beam section and has integral spring perches; the tie rod is in front of the axle. In the rear, the pressed-steel radius rods are secured against the frame rather than against the jackshaft.

The Museum's truck has a wheelbase of 156 inches, front tread of 68 inches, and rear tread of 78½ inches. The cast-steel wheels carry solid rubber tires—36 by 6 inches in front and 40 by 16 inches in the rear. An odometer, originally mounted in the hub of the left front wheel, is missing.

The 7-ton, steel dump body was raised by a Heil hydraulic hoist of the underbody type. This twin-cylinder hoist has an oil pump mounted centrally in front of the cylinders and a by-pass valve mounted at their rear. The cylinders are hung vertically but are free to rotate on trunnions mounted in the chassis frame in front of the rear axle. Direct-acting plungers that emerge from the tops of the cylinders connect with a transverse shaft mounted on the body's subframe.

To operate the hoist, the power take-off is engaged by depressing the clutch and moving forward a lever located to the left of the gear-change lever. This causes a shaft to rotate and drive the oil pump at the rear, but the oil merely flows in a circle until the operator closes the by-pass valve by moving a horizontal lever in front of the seat support on the right side of the cab. This diverts the oil into the cylinders, which then raise the body. The lower edge of a double-acting tail gate (which is hinged at top and bottom) is released by means of a lever on the left front corner of the body. The top part of the gate is released by removing two pins from the yokes that retain the upper-hinge pins.

Servi-Cycle

1935
Gift of Paul Treen in 1960

The 1935 Servi-Cycle.

The Museum's Servi-Cycle, designed by Paul Treen and built by the Simplex Manufacturing Corporation, of New Orleans, features simplicity in every respect. The motor bears the number 19351, indicating that it was built in 1935 and was the first of the series.

The single-cylinder, 2-cycle, 2-horsepower engine is air-cooled and equipped with a rotary valve. A tiny carburetor on the back of the motor was controlled by a wire operating from a knob located behind the steering head. A lever near the right grip operated a compression release for ease in starting. The operator opened the compression release with his right hand, pushed the cycle to gain speed, then closed the release to start the engine. A V-belt transmitted drive to the rear wheel.

There is no clutch, so the engine had to be switched off before the cycle could be stopped. Near the left grip is an electric button of the type generally used to operate a bicycle horn. The pressing of this button stopped the engine, apparently by shorting the low-tension side of the magneto, which is an Eisemann Model 71L bearing the serial number 2003.

The tires bear the name of the Simplex Manufacturing Company and are marked "26 x 2.250." An ordinary cycle coaster brake, made by Morrow, is operated by a pedal at the left of the engine. The bicycle's stand can be moved up to form a footrest.

The gasoline tank is in front of the seat, and the muffler is to the left of the rear wheel. An electric headlamp, mounted on the cycle's spring fork, received current from the magneto.

Bantam Truck

1940

Transferred from the United States War Department in 1944

In 1940 the American Bantam Car Company, Butler, Pennsylvania, constructed 62 quarter-ton, 4-wheel-drive trucks, prototypes of the famous Jeep which sometimes was called a "Peep" in its earlier days. Modified and standardized for volume production during World War II, many thousands of Jeeps were built by Willys-Overland Motors, Ford Motor Company, and the Bantam firm. Combining simplicity, exceptional mobility, reliability, low silhouette, and a capacity out of proportion to its small size, the Jeep proved to be such a versatile, successful, and familiar military vehicle that it seemed to symbolize the unity of the Allies during the war.

The Museum's Bantam, bearing serial number 1007, is the seventh of the 62 such trucks produced. It was delivered to the Army on November 29, 1940, and given the Army registration number W-2015330. Upon delivery to the Army Board at Fort Knox, Kentucky, it was put through a series of tests equivalent to about 100,000 miles of service and then was retired.

The Continental engine, of the 4-cylinder, L-head type, has a bore of $3\frac{3}{16}$ inches and a stroke of $3\frac{1}{2}$ inches and could develop 46 horsepower at 3,250 revolutions per minute. It is water-cooled, with a belt-driven fan and centrifugal water pump behind the radiator. All the electrical equipment on the engine —ignition coil and distributor, voltage regulator, generator, and starting motor—are by Auto-Lite. The 6-volt storage battery is beneath the hood, to the left of the engine.

A mechanical fuel pump and a fuel filter are used in conjunction with the constant-level, float-type carburetor, which is fitted with an air filter. A gear pump sent oil through a filter (on the cylinder head) to the engine's bearing surfaces, where it was kept under pressure.

The Bantam's weight is 2,700 pounds, its wheelbase 79 inches, and its tread 48 inches. The disk wheels, secured to the brake drums by five bolts, mount 16-by-5.50-inch tires. A spare wheel with tire could be carried at the back of the truck.

Four semielliptic springs, each with telescopic shock absorbers, connect the steel frame to the housings of the axles. The

The Army's Bantam truck of 1940, prototype of the famous Jeep.

frame is above the housings; the springs pass beneath them.

Power could be transmitted from the engine to all four wheels, but front-wheel drive was used only as necessary on difficult terrain. A transfer case, near the center of the frame and to the left of the transmission, provides passage of a drive shaft to the differential unit in the front-axle assembly. The shaft passes to the left of the engine, which is offset to the right in the frame. A similar shaft leads from the transfer case to the differential unit in the rear-axle assembly. Each differential unit contains spiral bevel gears, and each drive shaft has a universal joint at each end. The shaft to the front differential was controlled by means of two levers on the transfer case. The driver used the left lever to engage or disengage the front shaft while the rear one remained engaged, and he used the right lever to select low or high gear from the transfer case. The selective transmission, providing three speeds forward and a reverse, was controlled by a lever to the right of the two short levers on the transfer case. Final drive to the front wheels is by a shaft having a universal joint at each end of the front-axle housing.

The steering is of the conventional worm-and-follower type, with the tie bar connecting the front-wheel spindles, which are in front of the axle. Each of the two front-axle kingpins and each of the four brake drums is mounted on two tapered roller bearings. The right pedal actuated the master cylinder of the hydraulic brakes; the left pedal operated the disk clutch, which is between the engine flywheel and the transmission. The parking brake lever is under the instrument panel, on the left.

The 4-passenger body, constructed entirely of metal, has no doors—passengers stepped over the low sides to enter and leave the truck. Safety straps are attached at the outer side of each front seat. The Bantam has bumpers at front and rear and fenders over the front wheels; the body extends over the rear wheels. The folding windshield, of shatter-proof glass, has a hand-operated wiper on the left and a rear-view mirror at its base. The radiator is protected by a grillwork of vertical bars; and the hood, of the "clam-shell" type, is hinged at its back and has a single latch at the front. The gasoline tank is beneath the rear seat, and there is a rack for a fire extinguisher under the right-front seat. The top, constructed of pipe framework and canvas, is collapsible and can be removed easily.

The headlamps are mounted on the fenders, and next to each headlamp is a small auxiliary lamp designed for use in blackouts. All of the lamps are protected by grillwork. The beams of the headlights are controlled by a foot-operated button between the clutch and brake pedals. There is a lighting unit on the rear at each side. The one on the left provides a tail-light and a stop-light for general use and another tail-light for use in a blackout; the one on the right incorporates a tail-light and a stop-light for use in blackout. Reflectors are provided at the rear and on the sides near the back. A pintle hook, for towing purposes, is attached to the frame at the rear, and there are handles on each side of the body for use when the vehicle had to be assisted by manpower. A muffler runs to the rear of the body, beneath the right side.

The instrument panel contains a water-temperature gauge, oil-pressure gauge, electrically operated gasoline gauge, ammeter, speedometer, a starter button (at the left end of the panel) that actuates a solenoid attached to the starting motor, choke control, throttle control (supplementing the accelerator pedal), a light switch (in the center of the panel), and, just below it, a key-operated ignition switch.

The blackout lights were energized when the light switch was pulled out to the first position, and the service lights were turned on when the switch was pulled to the second position; however, to prevent accidental use of the service lights in a blackout, the operator had to push a release button at the side of the switch before it could be moved to the second position.

The Bantam has no manual ignition spark advance as the distributor incorporates a centrifugal automatic advance-and-retard mechanism. A button in the hub of the steering wheel operates the horn, which is mounted below the left headlamp.

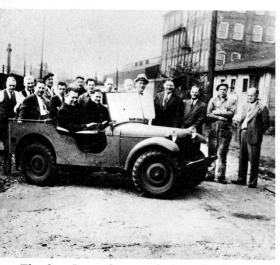

The first Jeep, photographed on the day it was completed at the Bantam plant at Butler, Pennsylvania, in October 1940. The fenders on this first truck were stock fenders for the Bantam automobile.

Chrysler Turbine Automobile

1964
Gift of Chrysler Corporation in 1967

In October 1963, after more than a decade of research on developing a gas-turbine automotive engine, Chrysler Corporation began a consumer evaluation study of 50 turbine-powered automobiles, of which the Museum's car is number 45. During the following two years the 50 cars were loaned to 203 persons, each for a period of three months, in order to test mechanical performance and consumer reaction. When the test program was completed in January 1966 the cars had been driven a total of more than a million miles.

The experimental automobile's principal feature is its 130-horsepower turbine engine, which has a performance equal to that of a 200-horsepower piston engine although it weighs only 410 pounds and has 80 percent fewer moving parts. Air is drawn into the engine and compressed by a centrifugal impeller. The compressed air is heated as it passes through two regenerators (heat exchangers), one on each side of the engine. Each of the 15-inch regenerator rotors contains a brazed, stainless-steel honeycomb, and each is driven mechanically by a cross

The Chrysler turbine automobile, 1964. (From a Chrysler Corporation photo.)

shaft geared to an accessory drive. Since the same turbine drives both the compressor and the accessories, the speed of the regenerators, varying between 9 and 22 revolutions per minute, is always proportionate to the speed of the compressor. Face-type seals separate the high-pressure and low-pressure sides of the regenerators.

From the regenerators the air passes into a combustion chamber (located under the engine) where the fuel is injected and ignited. The burning fuel raises the temperature of the gases and increases their energy level. The hot gases then pass through the first turbine, driving the compressor and accessories, and then through the second and larger turbine (independent of the first), driving the wheels. As the gases enter the second turbine they pass through a set of variable nozzle-vanes that turn at different angles so that the gases are directed at the optimum angle for maximum performance at any given engine speed. If the driver removes his foot from the accelerator at any speed over 15 miles an hour, the vanes turn to a reverse angle to provide engine braking.

On leaving the second turbine the gases pass through the low-pressure sides of the regenerators, where they transfer part of their heat to the incoming air. Finally, they pass through twin, rectangular, aluminum exhaust ducts, from which they emerge at a maximum temperature of about 500 degrees at full power. The engine is cooled by the surrounding air and by the compressed air that passes through it.

The starter-generator at the front of the engine is coupled directly to the accessory drive shaft. In starting, this unit rotates the gas generator and accessories until the engine fires and the first-stage turbine begins to accelerate under its own power.

Forced lubrication is provided by a pump that uses the same oil (Type A transmission oil) to lubricate engine, transmission, accessory drive, and reduction gear; at the same time the pump also provides hydraulic pressure for power steering, transmission control, and variable nozzle control. The fuel—which may be kerosene, diesel fuel, or unleaded gasoline—is carried in a 21-gallon tank at the rear.

To prevent overspeeding of the engine, the modified Torque-Flite 3-speed automatic transmission is equipped with a device that automatically upshifts when the control lever is in "low" and with a lock-up "idle" position of the control lever in place of "neutral." Since the power turbine is independent of the gas generator, no torque converter is required.

The propeller shaft connecting the transmission with the rear axle is 2¾ inches in diameter and has a ball-and-trunnion front universal joint and a cross-type rear joint. The standard 8¾-inch, 2-pinion rear axle has a 3.23 ratio.

Front suspension is on upper and lower control arms that

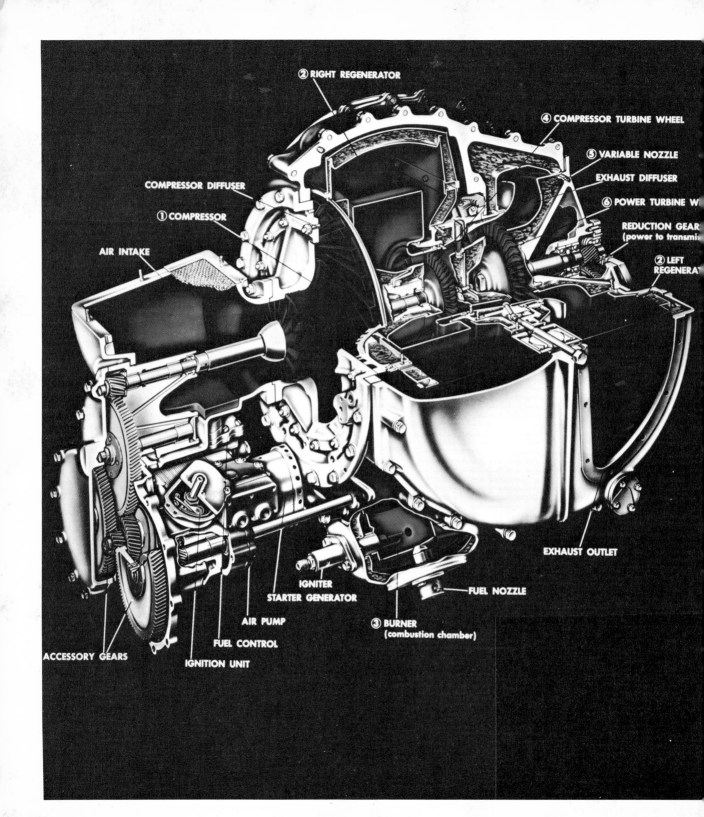

② RIGHT REGENERATOR

④ COMPRESSOR TURBINE WHEEL

⑤ VARIABLE NOZZLE

EXHAUST DIFFUSER

⑥ POWER TURBINE W

REDUCTION GEAR
(power to transmis

② LEFT
REGENERA

COMPRESSOR DIFFUSER

① COMPRESSOR

AIR INTAKE

EXHAUST OUTLET

IGNITER

STARTER GENERATOR

FUEL NOZZLE

AIR PUMP

③ BURNER
(combustion chamber)

ACCESSORY GEARS

FUEL CONTROL

IGNITION UNIT

have ball joints and a sway bar. The coil springs, acting against the lower control arm, contain shock absorbers. The suspension elements are attached to a large cross member by rubber-insulated mountings. Rear suspension is on two fore-and-aft 6-leaf springs and Oriflow shock absorbers.

The self-adjusting, servo-type power brakes operate in a drum (10 inches in diameter and 2½ inches wide) on each wheel. Parking brakes are provided by manual operation of the rear-wheel service brakes through a cable control.

The 2-door, "hardtop" body has two bucket seats in front and two in the rear. The drive shaft is housed within a hump in the floorboard that runs between the right and left seats. At the top of the raised area between the front seats is a console containing the gearshift selector, brake lever, and electrical switches for the various accessories. On the left side of the dash are three circular clusters of instruments. The left cluster contains a gauge for the turbine inlet temperature, ammeter, and oil-pressure gauge; the center one contains the speedometer and fuel gauge; and the right one contains a tachometer and clock. A push-button radio is in the center of the dash.

Power steering is through a column that is fitted with two universal joints. The low angle at which the steering column is set gives the driver a "sports-car feel."

The heater assembly, which is similar to that on the 1962 models of the Plymouth and Dodge, features an "instant heat" gas-to-air exchanger in which fresh air is heated by the hot gases from the turbine engine instead of by hot water.

The car weighs 3,900 pounds and has a 110-inch wheelbase, a tread of 59 inches in the front and 56.7 inches in the rear, and 7.50-by-14-inch, 4-ply, rayon tubeless tires.

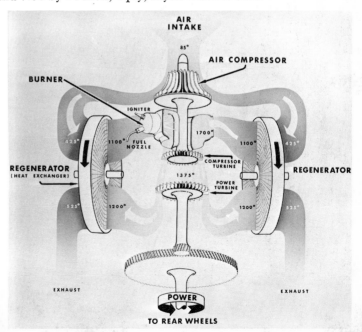

Diagram showing gas turbine operation of the experimental Chrysler of 1964; and (at left) main components of the twin-regenerator gas turbine. (From Chrysler Corporation photos.)

SELECTED REFERENCES

ALLEN, JAMES TITUS. *Digest of United States Patents: Air, Caloric, Gas and Oil Engines, 1789-1906.* 5 vols. (Washington: Columbia Planograph Co., 1907.)

ANDERSON, RUDOLPH E. *The Story of the American Automobile.* (Washington: Public Affairs Press, 1950.)

AUTOMOBILE MANUFACTURERS ASSOCIATION. *Automobiles of America.* (Detroit: Wayne State University Press, 1962.)

BATHE, GREVILLE, and DOROTHY BATHE. *Oliver Evans.* (Philadelphia: Historical Society of Pennsylvania, 1935.)

BEAUMONT, W. WORBY. *Motor Vehicles and Motors.* (Philadelphia: J. B. Lippincott, 1900.)

DENHAM, ATHEL F. *Twenty Years' Progress in Commercial Motor Vehicles.* (Detroit: Automotive Council for War Production, 1944.)

DIESEL, EUGEN, WITH GUSTAV GOLDBECK AND FRIEDRICH SCHILD-BERGER. *From Engines to Autos.* (Chicago: Henry Regnery, 1960.)

DOOLITTLE, JAMES R. *The Romance of the Automobile Industry.* (New York: Klebold Press, 1916.)

DOYLE, G. R. *The World's Automobiles.* (London: Temple Press, 1959.)

DYKE, A. L. *Dyke's Automobile and Gasoline Engine Encyclopedia.* (Various editions and publishers, 1911 through 1952.)

EDMONDS, J. P. *Gasoline Age.* (Lansing, Michigan: Franklin De Kleine, no date, about 1941.)

EPSTEIN, RALPH C. *The Automobile Industry: Its Economic and Commercial Development.* (New York: A. W. Shaw, 1928.)

FORBES, B. C., AND O. D. FOSTER. *Automotive Giants of America.* (New York: B. C. Forbes, 1926.)

FORWARD, E. A. *Catalog of the Collections in the Science Museum. Land Transport. II. Mechanical Road Vehicles.* (London: H. Majesty's Stationery Office, 1936.)

GREAT BRITAIN PARLIAMENT, HOUSE OF COMMONS. *Report on Steam Carriages by a Select Committee of the House of Commons of Great Britain.* (London: 1831.) [Reprinted as Document No. 101, 22d Congress, 1st Session, U. S. House of Representatives. (Washington: 1832).]

HARRISON, JOSEPH. *The Locomotive Engine, and Philadelphia's Share in Its Early Improvements.* (Philadelphia: George Gebbie, 1872.)

HAYNES, ELWOOD. *The Complete Motorist.* (Privately published, 1914.)

KURZEL-RUNTSCHEINER, ERICH. *Siegfried Marcus.* (Vienna: Technisches Museum für Industrie und Gewerbe, 1928.)

LONGSTREET, STEPHEN. *A Century on Wheels.* (New York: Henry Holt, 1952.)

MAXIM, HIRAM P. *Horseless Carriage Days.* (New York: Harper, 1937.)

NEVINS, ALLAN, WITH FRANK E. HILL. *Ford.* 3 vols. (New York: Scribners, 1954-1963.) [Vol. 1, *The Times, the Man, the Company,* 1954; vol. 2, *Expansion and Challenge,* 1957; vol. 3, *Decline and Rebirth,* 1963.]

NIEMEYER, GLENN A. *The Automotive Career of Ransom E. Olds.* (East Lansing, Michigan: Michigan State University, 1963.)

PAGE, VICTOR W. *Motorcycles and Side Cars.* (New York: Norman W. Henley, 1924.)

PARTRIDGE, BELLAMY. *Fill'er Up!* (New York: McGraw-Hill, 1952.)

POUND, ARTHUR. *The Turning Wheel.* (Garden City, New York: Doubleday, Doran, 1934.)

RAE, JOHN B. *American Automobile Manufacturers.* (New York: Chilton, 1959.)

RAE, JOHN B. *The American Automobile.* (Chicago: University of Chicago Press, 1965.)

SCOTT-MONCRIEFF, DAVID. *Three-Pointed Star—The Story of Mercedes-Benz Cars and Their Racing Successes.* (New York: W. W. Norton, 1956.)

SENNETT, A. R. *Carriages without Horses Shall Go.* (London: Whittaker, 1896.)

SHELDON, JAMES. *Veteran and Vintage Motor Cycles.* (London: B. T. Batsford, 1961.)

STERN, PHILIP VAN DOREN. *A Pictorial History of the Automobile.* (New York: Viking Press, 1953.)

THURSTON, ROBERT H. *A History of the Growth of the Steam-Engine.* (Ithaca, New York: Cornell University Press, 1939.)

TRAGATSCH, ERWIN. *The World's Motorcycles.* (London: Temple Press, 1964.)

WOODS, C. E. *The Electric Automobile.* (New York: Herbert S. Stone, 1900.)

In addition to the above, there are many periodicals—some no longer being published—that provide contemporary descriptions of automobiles and of racing and endurance contests. Such periodicals include the following:

The Automobile, first published in September 1899.

Automobile Trade Journal, which merged into *Motor Age* in 1928.

Automotive Industries, which started as *The Automobile.*

The Commercial Vehicle, first published in 1906.

Cycle and Automobile Trade Journal, which became *Automobile Trade Journal.*

The Horseless Age, first published in November 1895 and merged into *Motor Age* in 1918.

Motor, first published in 1903.

Motor Age, first published in September 1899.

Motor Life, first published in March 1906.

Power Wagon, first published in 1906.

Society of Automotive Engineers Journal, first published in April 1911 as *S. A. E. Bulletin.*

During the years 1904 through 1929, illustrated handbooks were issued annually by the Association of Licensed Automobile Manufacturers and its successors, the Automobile Board of Trade and the National Automobile Chamber of Commerce. These books, listing the major specifications of all the automobiles made by the members of those groups, are a valuable source of information. The Automobile Manufacturers Association, successor of the National Automobile Chamber of Commerce, publishes a pamphlet titled "Automobile Facts and Figures" that contains many statistics pertaining to the automobile industry.

Several clubs currently issue illustrated publications containing articles by authoritative writers, as well as reprinted articles from the old commercial periodicals. Publications of some of these clubs are as follows:

Air Cooled News, published three times yearly by The H. H. Franklin Club, Post Office Box 66, Onandaga Branch, Syracuse, New York. 13215.

Antique Automobile, published bimonthly by The Antique Automobile Club of America, West Drury Road, Hershey, Pennsylvania. 17033.

The Bulb Horn, published bimonthly by The Veteran Motor Car Club of America, Inc., 15 Newton Street, Brookline, Massachusetts. 02146.

The Classic Car, published quarterly by The Classic Car Club of America, Inc., 114 Liberty Street, New York, New York. 10006.

Horseless Carriage Club Gazette, published bimonthly by Horseless Carriage Club of America, 9031 East Florence Avenue, Arrington Square, Downey, California. 90240.

The Steam Automobile, published quarterly by Steam Automobile Club of America, Inc., 1937 East 71st Street, Chicago, Illinois. 60649.